Inte
Pu

Intelligent Puzzles

The UK Mensa Puzzle Editors
Ken Russell & Philip Carter

foulsham

LONDON • NEW YORK • TORONTO • SYDNEY

foulsham
Yeovil Road, Slough, Berkshire, SL1 4JH

ISBN 0-572-01806-1

Copyright © 1992 Kenneth Russell and Philip Carter

All rights reserved

The Copyright Act (1956) prohibits (subject
to certain very limited exceptions) the
making of copies of any copyright work or of
a substantial part of such a work, including
the making of copies by photocopying or
similar process. Written permission to make
a copy or copies must therefore normally be
obtained from the publisher in advance. It is
advisable also to consult the publisher if in
any doubt as to the legality of any copying
which is to be undertaken.

Phototypeset in Great Britain by Typesetting Solutions, Slough, Berks.
Printed in Great Britain by Cox & Wyman Ltd, Reading, Berks.

ABOUT MENSA

Mensa is a Social Club for which membership is accepted from all persons with an IQ of 148 or above. This represents 2% of the population. Therefore, one person in 50 is capable of passing the entrance examination, which consists of a series of intelligence tests.

Mensa is the Latin word for 'table'. We are a round-table society, where all persons are equal.

Mensa has three aims: social contact amongst intelligent people; research in psychology; and the identification and fostering of intelligence.

Mensa is an International Society and has 102 000 members of all occupations: clerks, doctors, lawyers, policemen, industrial workers, teachers, nurses, etc.

Enquiries to: MENSA FREEPOST
WOLVERHAMPTON WV2 1BR

MENSA INTERNATIONAL
15 The Ivories,
6–8 Northampton Street,
LONDON N1 2HV

ABOUT THE AUTHORS

Ken Russell is a London Surveyor and is Puzzle Editor of the *British Mensa Magazine*, a magazine which is sent to its 40 000 British members monthly.

Philip Carter is a JP and an Estimator from Yorkshire. He is Puzzle Editor of *Enigmasig*, the monthly newsletter of the Mensa Puzzle Special Interest group.

ACKNOWLEDGEMENTS

We are indebted to our wives, both named Barbara, for checking and typing the manuscript, and for their encouragement in our various projects.

PUZZLE AND ANSWER NUMBERING

So that you don't inadvertently read the answer to the next puzzle while you are checking your solution, the answers are numbered in a different sequence from that of the puzzles.

Each puzzle has a Puzzle Number and an Answer Number. Each answer has an Answer Number and a Puzzle Number. These are also listed on page 122, immediately before the Answers section.

STAR RATING OF PUZZLES

★ Standard
★★ Difficult
★★★ Very Difficult

This star rating is given only as a guide. Obviously, different readers will find different puzzles simple or difficult.

★★ 1 JUMBLE I

Commencing always with the centre letter 'D', spell out eight 11-letter words, travelling in any direction, but always to an adjacent square, horizontally, vertically or diagonally. Each letter, apart from the centre letter 'D', may be used only once.

E	E	D	N	E	S	S	O	N
C	L	T	F	I	C	T	I	R
R	I	O	V	I	A	T	E	I
N	C	S	E	E	E	C	R	O
E	D	S	R	**D**	O	U	A	T
O	D	E	O	O	O	M	E	E
R	N	W	R	O	M	I	N	T
T	K	C	K	N	I	E	N	A
R	E	O	N	G	R	E	Y	R

(ANSWER 101)

7

★ 2 GREAT WORDS

All the following are synonyms of 'GREAT'. When you
have solved them, rearrange the first letters of each to find
a ninth synonym of 'GREAT'.

    _ O _ L _
    _ L _ R _ O _ S
    _ U _ U _ T
    _ R _ M _ N _ O _ S
    _ O _ O _ S _ L
    _ M _ E _ S _
    _ L _ U _ T _ I _ U _
    _ R _ N _

(ANSWER 107)

★ 3 ALPHABET X-WORD I

Place the letters of the alphabet in the X-Word to complete the words, using each letter once only.

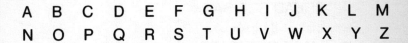

A B C D E F G H I J K L M
N O P Q R S T U V W X Y Z

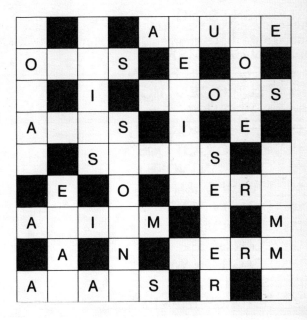

(ANSWER 113)

★ 4 LETTER CHANGE

Change one letter from each word to make, in each case, a well-known phrase, for example:

PET RICE QUACK = GET RICH QUICK

1   BREAD SHE SANK
2   SEND IN FAR
3   MAKE SO HEARD
4   ME FORT
5   WISH I SANG
6   DOT I HOLE
7   AN HAT LATER
8   DEEP FOUR FAIR IN
9   FLOP O DEAR HOUSE
10 SO SO HOT
11 MADE CRACKS FAR
12 PULP O LAST ODE
13 O DIG ON I JOKE
14 BALL IF WISH
15 CAN ON SAND
16 LIFE IS US
17 PLAN SALE
18 PEACH ON WIND
19 IS FALL SWINE
20 BURN US TRAMPS

(ANSWER 119)

★★ 5 *THREE TOO MANY*

Delete three of the four given letters in each case, to complete the crossword.

(ANSWER 125)

★ 6 *QUICK CALCULATION*

Without the use of a calculator, or of pencil and paper, how can you quickly calculate, in your head, the sum of all the numbers from 1 to 100 inclusive?

(ANSWER 131)

★★★ 7 GROUPS I

These group names have been mixed up. Can you sort them?

MURDER	of	GEESE
KNOT	of	HARES
LABOUR	of	TOADS
GAGGLE	of	CROWS
MUSTER	of	MOLES
HUSK	of	PEACOCKS

(ANSWER 137)

★ 8 FIND THE LOGIC

14		7	4
	12	9	16
10	15	5	13
6	8	11	

The numbers 4 – 16 have already been inserted into the grid, almost, but not quite at random.

Following just two simple rules, where would you place the numbers 1, 2 and 3 in the grid?

(ANSWER 143)

★★★ 9 PRONOUNS

The word CHEWED contains two complete Pronouns in
letter order: HE   and   WE.

Find a 6-letter word which contains five complete
pronouns in letter order.

(*ANSWER* 149)

★★ 10 WORD CONNECTIONS

Each pair of words, by meaning or association, leads to
another word. Fill in words 18–30 to arrive at the final
word 'SOAP'. The number of dots indicates the number of
letters in the missing word.

1 SHIP	17 VESSEL				
2 UTENSIL		25			
3 REPOSITORY	18				
4 STALK			29 ...		
5 AXE	19				
6 FIELD		26			
7 ACTION	20				31 SOAP
8 ENCOUNTER					
9 PEACE	21				
10 EUPHONY		27			
11 TUNE	22				
12 NOTE			30		
13 JOY	23				
14 SORROW		28			
15 PLAY	24				
16 HOSPITAL					

(*ANSWER* 1)

★ 11 TILES I

Fit the nine tiles together to make a Crossword.

(ANSWER 11)

★★ 12 SEQUENCE I

What is the next number in this sequence?

21
4221
63
84424221
105
12663

(ANSWER 21)

★★ 13 LOGIC

Place the numbers 1 to 16 in the grid according to the instructions.

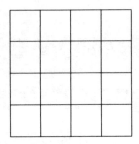

1	is	two places above 14 and one place to the left of 9.
3	is	three places below 5.
1	is	two places right of 6.
9	is	two places above 3.
11	is	three places to the left of 5.
4	is	one place to the right of 11.

②—⑬
⑫—⑦   form a block together.

10	is	one place below 4.
8 and 15		are adjacent.
16	is	next to 5.

(ANSWER 31)

★ 14 *COMMON CLUES*

What do the answers to all of these clues have in common?

1 Type of Book-keeping System.
2 Incomprehensible Talk.
3 Action characterised by Treachery.
4 Verification.
5 Gibberish.
6 Type of Omnibus.
7 Type of Stringed Instrument.
8 Spy.
9 Rapid.
10 Betray.

(ANSWER 41)

★★★ **15 ZOETROPE**

Find a 3-letter word on the Inner Scale which, when transposed on to the Outer Scale, will produce another 3-letter word. For example: G on the Inner Scale corresponds to W on the Outer Scale; O on the Inner Scale corresponds to E on the Outer Scale. So the word GO on the Inner Scale becomes WE on the Outer Scale.

Then try 4- and 5-letter words.

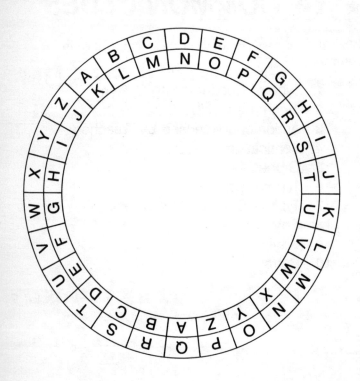

(ANSWER 51)

★ 16 COLOUR MATCH

I have a calendar where each day of the week is shaded a different colour. All the MONDAYS are shaded ORANGE and all the THURSDAYS are shaded BLUE. What colour are all the TUESDAYS shaded?

(ANSWER 61)

★★★ 17 A RIDDLE FROM SOUTH AFRICA

It is coloured and round.
It has a pot-belly.
It lies on the ground.
It blows at a fellow.
A dog it kisses.
And kills while it hisses.

What is it?

(ANSWER 71)

★★ 18 NO REPEAT LETTERS

The grid below contains 25 different letters of the alphabet. What is the longest word which can be found by starting anywhere and working from square to square horizontally, vertically or diagonally and not repeating a letter?

Q	U	D	M	X
V	J	A	G	Y
P	H	E	T	S
N	L	R	I	F
B	O	W	K	C

(ANSWER 81)

★★★ 19 COLOURS

What are the chances that 4 White balls are drawn from a bag when 4 are drawn at random from the contents of

        10 White
          4 Black
and   3 Red?

(ANSWER 91)

★★ 20 PYRAMID QUOTATION

'OFTEN THE IMPOSSIBLE IS WHAT HAS NEVER BEEN ATTEMPTED.'

Using all 45 letters of the above sentence, complete the Pyramid with 1 × 1-letter, 1 × 2-letter, 1 × 3-letter, 1 × 4-letter, 1 × 5-letter, 1 × 6-letter, 1 × 7-letter, 1 × 8-letter and 1 × 9-letter word.

Clues are given, but in no particular order.

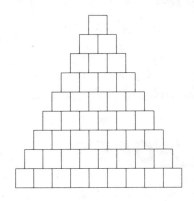

Spring on one foot.

Inhabitant.

Main topic of a book.

Symbol for the fourth note of the scale of C Major.

Military unit.

To 'Sugar the Pill'.

Woman who deliberately allures men.

Live, exist.

Written work submitted for degree.

(ANSWER 2)

★★★ 21 FLANNEGAN'S FINAGLING FACT

(There is a clue to the keying of this Cryptogram in this title.)

JMCJ SUCDJHJY WMHIM, WMED
PUBJHRBHEL KY, LHVHLEL KY, CLLEL JQ, QT
GUKJTCIJEL ATQP JME CDGWET YQU FEJ,
FHVEG YQU JME CDGWET YQU GMQUBL
MCVE FQJJED.

(ANSWER 12)

★★ 22 WORDS I

What have these words in common?

AS,   HOSE,   TIER,   SALE.

(ANSWER 22)

★★★ 23 ALPHABET CROSSWORD I

Using all 26 letters of the alphabet, complete the grid. Five letters are already placed.

A B C D E F̸ G H I J̸ K L M
N O P Q̸ R S T U V W X̸ Y̸ Z

(ANSWER 32)

★★★ **24** *TARGET*

Charlie hits the target
   80 times in 100 shots.

Jim hits the target
   90 times in 100 shots.

What are the chances that the target is hit, if each fires
once?

(ANSWER 42)

★★★ 25 CRAZY COLUMNS

Insert the missing numbers in the following table.

0	2	1	3
3	6	1	5
1	7	6	9
10	12	2	11
3		15	15
21	18	5	17
	19	28	21
36	24	13	23
21	29		27
55	30	34	31
55	37	66	
78	36	89	41

(ANSWER 52)

★★★ **26 RIDDLE**

My first two letters are a man,
My first three a woman,
My first four a brave man,
My whole a brave woman.

What am I?

(ANSWER 62)

★ 27 WORD CIRCLE

Place the letters in the correct boxes in each quadrant to obtain two 8-letter words, one reading clockwise and the other anticlockwise. The two words are synonyms.

NW: NAOI
NE: EYDR
SW: RCDI
SE: RMEO

(ANSWER 72)

★★ 28 LETTERS

The four letters S, E, N, T, are placed in a row at random. What is the probability that an English word is formed?

(ANSWER 82)

★★★ 29 MAGIC WITHIN MAGIC WITHIN MAGIC

Insert the remaining numbers from 1 to 64 in such a way that a magic 8 × 8 square is formed where each horizontal, vertical and corner-to-corner line totals 260. Within that is a magic 6 × 6 square where each horizontal, vertical and corner-to-corner line totals 195, and within that is a magic 4 × 4 square where each horizontal, vertical and corner-to-corner line totals 130.

			5				
	15					20	
55		25					10
		30					
			35				
				40			
	45					50	
			60				

(ANSWER 92)

★ **30** *MIDDLE WORDS*

Fill in the missing word which, when tacked on to the first word, forms a new word and, when placed in front of the second word, forms another word. The number of dashes indicates the number of letters in the missing word.

For instance: SEA __ __ __ NET; answer SON, to give the new words SEASON and SONNET.

1 PUMP __ __ __ SHIP
2 PIT __ __ RUSH
3 ROLL __ __ __ __ BAND
4 TEA __ __ __ __ LET
5 MODE __ __ __ __ ABLE
6 WAR __ __ __ __ UP
7 HEAT __ __ __ ON
8 CAR __ __ __ TEN
9 FOND __ __ __ HER
10 LEG __ __ __ __ PIPE

(ANSWER 3)

★★ 31 TARGET CROSSWORD I

Find sixteen 6-letter words by pairing up the thirty-two 3-letter bits.

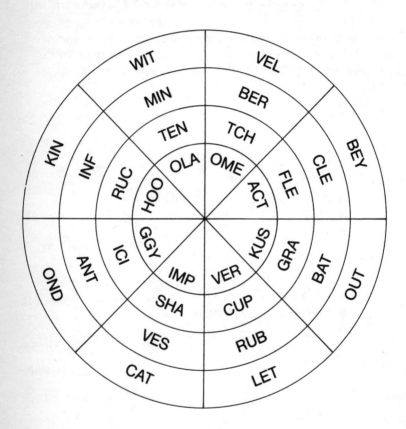

(ANSWER 13)

★ 32 HIDDEN ANAGRAM I

If we presented you with the words 'MAR', 'AM', and 'FAR' and asked you to find the shortest English word which contained all the letters from which these words could be produced, we would expect you to come up with the word 'FARM'. Here is a further list of words:

GRAND, CORD, BURN, KNOB

What is the shortest English word from which all these four words can be produced?

(*ANSWER* 23)

★★ 33 MEASLE FISH

In my lake there are 4998 Measle Fish. The Male fish each have 111 Spots whilst the Females each have 37 Spots.

I take out ⅔ of the Male fish and count all of the Spots on the remaining fish. How many spots do I count?

(*ANSWER* 33)

★★ 34 MINERALS

Start at the middle square and move from square to square horizontally, vertically and diagonally to spell out six types of Minerals. Use every square in the grid only once and finish at the top right-hand square.

T	E	X	U	A	T	E	→ END
A	I	A	M	L	I	H	
T	L	A	B	E	A	C	
E	S	B	★	T	I	R	
R	C	A	N	G	L	Y	
U	R	O	M	I	A	P	
N	D	U	I	S	S	S	

(ANSWER 43)

★★ 35 COMPLETE THE CALCULATION

Insert the same number twice to make this calculation correct.

$$6 \div 8 = 27$$

(ANSWER 53)

★★ 36 PYRAMID I

Spell out the 15-letter word by going into the Pyramid one room at a time. Go into each room once only. You may go into the passage as many times as you wish.

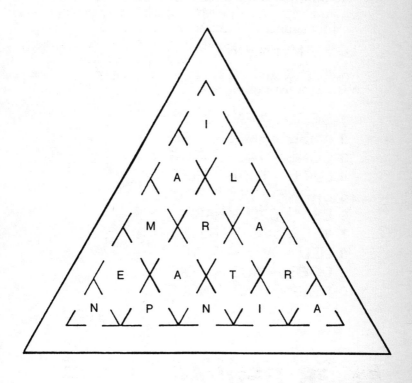

(ANSWER 63)

★★ 37 ANAGRAMMED SYNONYMS

In each of the following, study the list of three words. Your task is to find two of the three words which can be paired to form an anagram of one word which is a synonym of the word remaining. For example:

LEG - MEEK - NET

The words 'LEG' and 'NET' are an anagram of 'GENTLE', which is a synonym of the word remaining 'MEEK'.

1 DISC - PLEA - SHIFT
2 AMBLE - MEAN - RISE
3 CONE - TALE - DATE
4 LUCK - TORE - FUN
5 CRONE - DUEL - TUNE
6 ERA - BAD - RASP
7 YET - VEER - ROOM
8 LIED - ACT - FORT
9 DOER - VICE - HEAR
10 PEAL - TEAR - NOSE

(ANSWER 73)

★★ 38 CEREAL

A box of cereal was on sale for 96p. The percentage profit made by the supermarket had the same numerical value as the cost, in pence, to the supermarket.

How much did it cost the supermarket?

(ANSWER 83)

★★ 39 SEQUENCE II

Can you draw the next figure in this sequence?

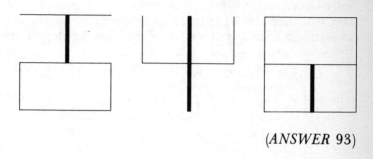

(*ANSWER* 93)

★★ 40 CRYPTOGRAM I

This is a straight substitution Cryptogram where each letter of the alphabet has been replaced by another.

SJLZL XE RC VDR AXWXRQ PJC XER'S
YDIDMAL CT FCXRQ VCZL SJDR JL SJXRNE
JL YDR FC.
JLRZH TCZF

(*ANSWER* 4)

The answers are all 9-letter words and will be found in the grid, one letter on each line, in order. Each letter is used only once.

P	P	T	M	H	T	P	S	N
O	E	E	A	R	O	R	H	E
Q	X	D	I	N	V	R	L	O
I	U	E	E	M	M	I	M	E
T	N	N	A	M	E	Y	I	E
N	A	C	E	S	N	E	N	S
I	T	T	O	E	T	T	T	I
E	N	E	I	A	M	E	E	S
M	C	D	R	T	R	L	B	R

1 Bee's store.
2 Fare meter.
3 Frenzy.
4 Occuring every ninth year.
5 To set aside.
6 Standing out.
7 Three months.
8 Contemplated.
9 A card game.

(ANSWER 14)

★★★ 42 SOMETHING'S THE SAME

What do the following 7-letter words have in common?

BRACKET, CAPABLE, SPICING, CRANIUM, REWRITE.

(ANSWER 24)

★★★ 43 MAGIC NUMBER SQUARE

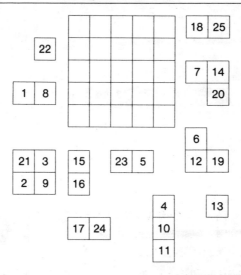

Place the tiles in the square so that each across line, each down line, and each of the diagonals, adds up to 65.

(ANSWER 34)

★★★ 44 ANAGRAM THEME I

Arrange the 14 words in pairs so that each pair is an anagram of another word or name. The seven words produced will have a linking theme. For example, if the words 'TRY' and 'CREASE' appeared in the list, they could be paired to form the word 'SECRETARY' and the theme could be PROFESSIONS.

AIL	HAD	NIB	SHIN
ALE	INCH	PIN	SIN
ANGER	LEG	SASH	
GALE	MET	SEAL	

(ANSWER 44)

★★★ 45 REBUS I

Find the word.

(ANSWER 54)

★★ 46 THREE NAMES

What have the following names in common?

OSWALD
CLAIRE
PIERRE

(ANSWER 64)

★★ 47 SQUARE I

Divide the Square into four identical sections. Each section must contain the same 9 letters, which can be arranged into a familiar 9-letter word.

T	E	E	S	I	R
V	R	E	V	I	S
E	E	I	T	E	V
S	E	E	E	E	T
T	T	I	T	V	E
R	R	S	E	T	T

(ANSWER 74)

★ 48 FAMILY

"Relationships are funny," remarked Bob. "Terence is the same relation to you that I am to your son."

"So he is," Clarence chuckled. "And you're the same relation to me that Terence is to you."

What relation was Clarence to Terence?

(*ANSWER* 84)

★ 49 CROSS-ALPHABET

Insert the 26 letters of the alphabet into the grid, once each only, to form a Crossword. Clues are given, but in no particular order.

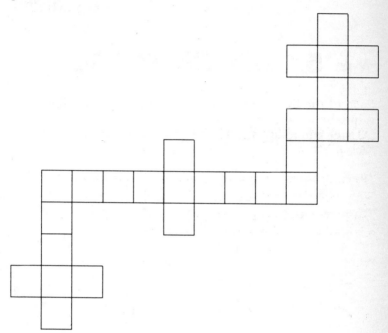

Clues:

Type of cuttlefish.
Covered vehicle.
Thrust with stick.
Trot along.
Excessively sentimental.
Make firm.
Mesh of fine threads.
Dryly humorous.

(ANSWER 94)

★★ **50** *THREE DICE*

What are the chances of throwing exactly 15 in one throw with three dice?

(ANSWER 5)

★★ **51** *BLOCK TOTAL*

Each of the five letters in the Word Block has a different value, between one and nine.

Using the totals next to the grid, work out the value of each letter.

F	I	V	E	S	26
F	V	S	F	F	29
I	V	S	S	S	24
I	E	E	S	V	22
V	E	I	F	F	29

34 27 23 20 26

(ANSWER 15)

★ **52** *SEQUENCE II*

What is the next number in this sequence?

1, 64, 729, 4096,   ?   ,

(ANSWER 25)

★★★ 53 'E' FRAME

Each horizontal and vertical line contains the consonants of a word, not necessarily in order. The word can be completed by adding a number of 'E' vowels. The number 33 at the end of each line indicates that each word you are looking for has 3 consonants and 3 'E' vowels.

Each letter in the grid may be used only once and all letters must be used.

Down

	1	2	3	4	5	6	
1	L	C	H	D	R	R	33
2	C	F	S	L	D	N	33
3	N	M	R	G	W	V	33
4	T	R	W	S	L	Y	33
5	D	B	L	T	P	R	33
6	C	L	Z	S	S	H	33

Across (label on left side)

33 33 33 33 33 33

Clues:
Across
1 Law.
2 Give up.
3 Come out.
4 Part of needle.
5 Insect.
6 A food.

Down
1 To sew with.
2 Part of insect.
3 Spoof.
4 Renter.
5 One who cries.
6 Thin layer of wood.

(ANSWER 35)

★ 54 SOMETHING IN COMMON I

What do the following words all have in common?

MANY, RAIN, KEY, WAIT, WAY.

(ANSWER 45)

★★ 55 DOG

My Dog and Kennel cost £25.

If the Dog had cost £5 more, the Kennel would have been a third of the total.

If the Kennel had been £5 less, I would have spent ¾ of the total on the Dog.

What did the Dog cost?

(ANSWER 55)

★★ 56 CRYPTOGRAM II

This is a straight substitution Cryptogram, where each letter of the alphabet has been replaced by another.

N WKKO RGRKDT SU BKZ NU WKKO NU N HSZZHG SBL.
FMSBGUG VDKEGDX

(ANSWER 65)

★★ 57 MONEY

Jack had 75p and three-quarters of what Jill had.
 Jill had 50p and half of what Jack had.

How much did each have?

(ANSWER 75)

★★ 58 PYRAMID WORD I

Solve the five clues. Enter the correct words in the Pyramid and then rearrange all the letters to find a 15-letter word.

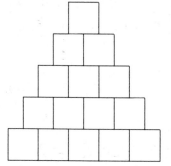

The pronoun of the first person singular. (1)

Objective case singular of first personal pronoun. (2)

Young man. (3)

Precipitation. (4)

Underground room. (5)

(ANSWER 85)

★★★ 59 CARGO BOAT

Statistics, in 1946, showed that 2% of fruit boats arrived with their cargoes ruined.

If two boats arrived, what was the probability that:

(a) Both cargoes were ruined?
(b) Only one was ruined?
(c) Neither was ruined?

(ANSWER 95)

★★★ 60 A TOUR OF THE USA

Track from square to square horizontally, vertically or diagonally to spell out the names of 22 American States. Use each square once, and once only. It does not matter which State you identify first. Providing you make the correct turnings, the 22 names will eventually lead you through the pattern of all 169 letters.

Y	W	N	O	H	L	K	B	A	L	A	I	R
O	A	A	M	A	O	C	A	M	A	E	O	G
I	M	T	N	A	T	N	O	A	P	N	N	E
N	G	M	O	M	U	O	N	V	L	S	N	G
T	S	U	A	C	E	N	G	A	A	Y	A	A
T	E	H	S	I	C	E	N	I	V	I	I	S
S	D	E	C	S	T	R	N	O	E	D	N	A
E	R	A	L	A	O	D	I	T	M	R	A	S
T	E	N	W	A	O	A	A	I	W	A	N	K
O	E	S	N	E	H	W	O	I	A	I	I	R
E	H	I	S	P	P	S	V	R	H	A	N	A
S	I	M	O	I	A	I	I	G	A	O	S	A
S	I	S	S	X	E	T	N	I	L	I	U	I

(ANSWER 6)

★★★ 61 MISSING LETTERS I

Find the words below. Each is a Coin, or Coins.

1 _ O _ I _ I _ N _
2 _ E _ T _ V _
3 _ U _ L _ E _
4 _ E _ T _ R _ I _ M
5 _ O _ E _ E _ G _
6 _ O _ E _ K
7 _ A _ O _ E _ N
8 _ C _ I _ L _ N _
9 _ E _ T _ R _ I _
10 _ O _ B _ E

(ANSWER 16)

★★★ 62 SYNCHRONISED SYNONYMS

Each grid contains the letters of eight 8-letter words. All letters are in the correct order and each letter is used once only. Each word in Grid One has a Synonym in Grid Two and the letters of each of the eight pairs of Synonyms are in exactly the same position in each grid. Clues to each pair of Synonyms are given, in no particular order.

Example: The answers to the clue 'MEEKNESS', are the words 'DOCILITY' in Grid One and 'MILDNESS' in Grid Two.

GRID ONE

F	C	C	M	D	C	O	E
A	N	(D)	X	R	Y	E	O
T	I	N	F	(O)	C	R	T
H	T	E	I	I	E	R	I
T	L	N	(C)	I	N	N	I
V	(I)	U	D	E	(L)	I	I
N	L	(I)	C	S	A	E	(T)
L	T	E	E	(Y)	S	Y	G

GRID TWO

O	L	I	R	E	S	N	R
L	T	Ⓜ	I	B	O	X	E
M	L	N	P	Ⓘ	V	A	R
A	G	P	T	E	I	I	L
T	D	G	Ⓛ	N	I	H	G
U	Ⓓ	E	I	A	Ⓝ	I	C
N	N	Ⓔ	T	S	I	E	Ⓢ
C	I	N	T	Ⓢ	H	G	G

Clues:
Meekness
Fanciful
Specific
Gripping
Gracious
Conspire
Slipshod
Protract

(ANSWER 26)

★★★ 63 SENTENCE

Many men will only sup shandy, yet gin or rum, may be in gross supply.

What is strange about this sentence?

(ANSWER 36)

★ 64 LOGIC ANALOGY I

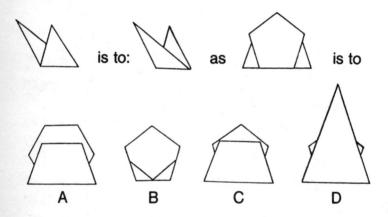

A   B   C   D

(ANSWER 46)

★★ 65 DOG RACE

In a race of 6 greyhounds, in how many ways can the 6 dogs pass the post? (**Example:** 6, 3, 2, 1, 4, 5, would be one way.)

(ANSWER 56)

Insert the numbers 0-11 in the circles, so that for any particular circle the sum of the numbers in the circles connected directly to it equals the value corresponding to the number in that circle, as given in the list below.

Example:

1	=	14 (4+7+3)
4	=	8 (7+1)
7	=	5 (4+1)
3	=	1

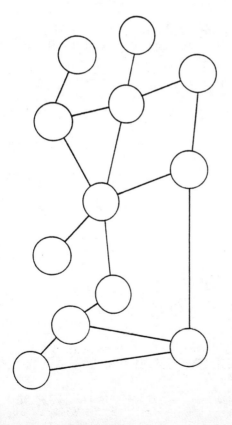

0	=	15
1	=	31
2	=	14
3	=	7
4	=	18
5	=	1
6	=	14
7	=	19
8	=	2
9	=	1
10	=	4
11	=	13

(ANSWER 66)

51

★★★ 67 BOOKS

"The Red Books are 49p each and the Blue Books are 39p each," said the shop assistant. "The total cost is £5.25." "It should be £5.27," said the customer.

How many Red Books and how many Blue Books were there?

(ANSWER 76)

★★ 68 MAGIC SQUARE I

Transfer the 25 letters to the blank grid to form a Magic Word Square where the five 5-letter words read the same both across and down.

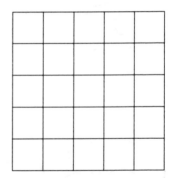

A	A	E	E	K
M	M	N	N	O
O	O	O	P	P
R	R	R	R	S
S	S	T	T	T

(ANSWER 86)

★ 69 DICE

Two dice are thrown together. What are the chances that they will score more than 9?

(ANSWER 96)

★ 70 THE LARGEST CIRCLE

What is the Largest Circle which you can fit in the Square which meets the following conditions?

1 It must be larger than any circle already in the square.

2 It must not touch the side of another circle.

3 It must not overlap the side of the square.

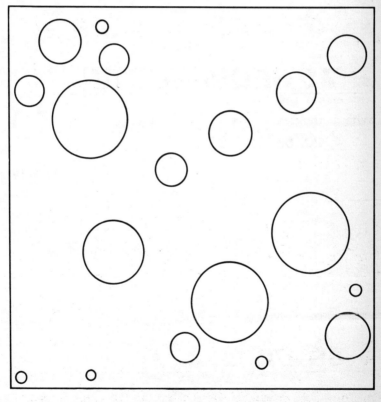

(*ANSWER 7*)

★ 71 SEQUENCE IV

What is the next number in this sequence?

4, 20, 56, 120, 220,　　?　,

(ANSWER 17)

★★★ 72 *DIY X-WORD*

Place the letters and groups of letters and blanks, below, in the grid to complete the X-Word.

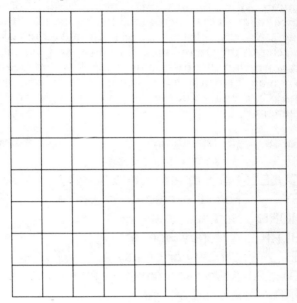

S L	E W	L A	P ■	A P
T ■	A P	O E	■ R	A C
■ T	E ■	■ S	P ■	E ■
N O	■ W	■ B	N E	L I

I M P	S ■ S	A ■ L	E N T
C R I	R U D	■ M ■	R ■ B
H E N	D G Y	■ P E	

P	I	T	P
■	S	T	P

(ANSWER 27)

★★ 73 NOVEL WORD POWER

In Column (A) is a list of words. The problem is to rearrange them so that their initial letters spell out the name of a Novel published in 1984. To make the task easier, refer to the Definition Column (B) and put the correct word with that definition in the Answers Column (C). When all the words have been correctly placed, in Column (C), the title will then appear reading down the initial letters.

(A) Words	(B) Definitions	(C) Answers
TRACT	A woman's fur cape	
RETICULE	Pride or arrogance	
PURSY	Formal expression of praise	
LEGHORN	Soft and limp	
HAUBERK	A literary word for west	
TIPPET	Slippery or greasy	
ENCOMIUM	A woman's small bag	
CHILIAD	A court official	
HUBRIS	A long coat of mail	
OAKUM	Short-winded	
FLACCID	A strip of pleated lace	
RUCHE	Expressing choice or wish	
OCCIDENT	A religious pamphlet	
TIPSTAFF	A bay window	
UNCTUOUS	One thousand years	
ORIEL	Loose fibre	
OPTATIVE	Italian straw	

(ANSWER 37)

★ 74 ENIGMAGRAM

Solve the four Anagrams of Drinks. Transfer the arrowed letters and solve the fifth Anagram.

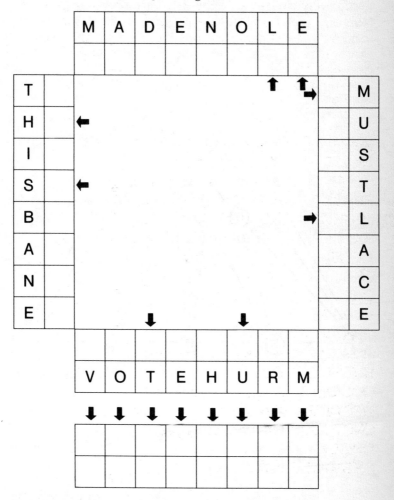

(ANSWER 47)

★ 75 NETWORK I

Start anywhere and travel along the connecting lines in a continuous path to adjacent circles to spell out a 14-letter word. Every circle must be visited once only.

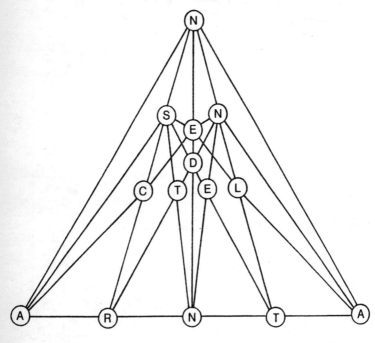

(ANSWER 57)

★★ 76 GROUP PUZZLE

Arrange the following words into groups of three.

LESS	BLOOD	OVER
STEP	TING	FREE
MARKS	NESS	PING
CARE	SHIP	MAN
THIN	LET	KING

(ANSWER 67)

★ 77 SEQUENCE V

Which figure is missing from this sequence?

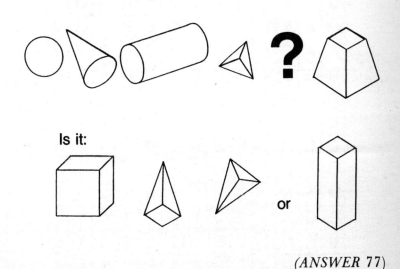

Is it:

or

(ANSWER 77)

★★ 78 CONCENTRATION

A B C D E F G H

Which letter is two to the right of the letter which is three
to the left of the letter immediately to the left of the letter
three to the right of the letter two to the left of the letter
four to the right of the letter immediately to the left of the
letter which is three to the left of the letter which comes
mid-way between the letter three to the right of the letter
'E' and the letter immediately to the right of the letter 'C'?

(ANSWER 87)

★ 79 X-WORD I

In the X-Word below, all of the black squares have been
replaced with letters. You have to find the black squares.

S	A	L	U	T	E	N	S	C	R	I	M	P
U	P	I	T	R	A	L	L	Y	E	N	O	A
G	A	N	N	E	T	I	O	S	P	R	E	Y
A	A	G	E	K	E	M	P	T	R	O	V	E
R	E	E	L	K	R	O	E	N	D	A	T	E
S	A	R	E	E	L	P	R	K	U	D	O	S
E	V	E	M	A	T	T	R	I	P	U	T	S
D	E	M	U	R	E	N	O	D	E	T	E	R
U	S	E	R	T	H	I	S	I	S	A	M	E
M	I	N	T	C	I	L	L	A	L	M	A	A
D	O	T	T	E	D	I	E	X	T	E	N	D
U	R	O	L	L	E	V	E	L	I	S	T	E
M	U	R	A	L	S	A	T	E	E	T	E	R

(ANSWER 97)

★★ 80 *ODD ONE OUT*

Which one is the odd one out?

   LOVE, FALL, ILL, AGE, ACE.

(ANSWER 8)

★★ 81 *HEXAGON I*

Fit the listed words into the six spaces encircling the
appropriate number on the diagram so that each word
correctly interlinks with the two words on either side (you
will see that each word has two consecutive letters in
common with the word on its side). (**Note**: to arrive at the
correct solution some words will have to be entered
clockwise and some anticlockwise.)

DEATHS
STAPLE
EITHER
STRIPE
DEBRIS
PLIERS
BIRDIE
VENICE
KEENER
BREVET
RENEWS
NICKED

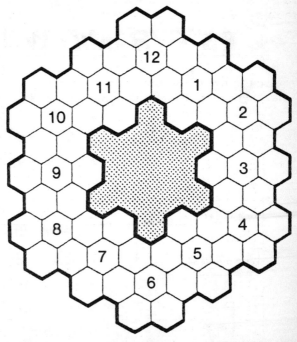

(ANSWER 18)

★★★ 82 WHAT'S IN A NAME?

Arrange the following Girls' and Boys' Names into groups of three.

OLIVE   ISABEL
PRIMROSE   MYRTLE
GARNET   DIAMOND
PEARL   SANDY
MARTIN   MAVIS
ROBIN   POPPY

(ANSWER 28)

★★ 83 PYRAMID WORD II

Solve the five clues. Enter the correct words in the Pyramid and then rearrange all the letters to find a 15-letter word.

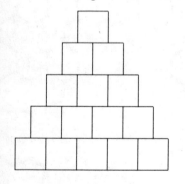

An exclamation. (1)

Enclosed. (2)

Surpass. (3)

Tuber. (4)

Cause sharp pain. (5)

(ANSWER 38)

★★★ **84 ALLSORTS**

Arrange the following into groups of four.

FYLFOT	TERPSICHORE
PRUDENCE	URANIA
CAPRICORN	HERALD
ERMINE	CANCER
CALLIOPE	TEMPERANCE
EUTERPE	FORTITUDE
SCORPIO	LIBRA
CHEVRON	CHARITY

(ANSWER 48)

★★ 85 REVOLVING I

Complete the word in each column; all the words end in 'R'.

The scrambled letters in the section to the right of each column are an anagram of a word which will give you a clue to the word you are trying to find, in the column.

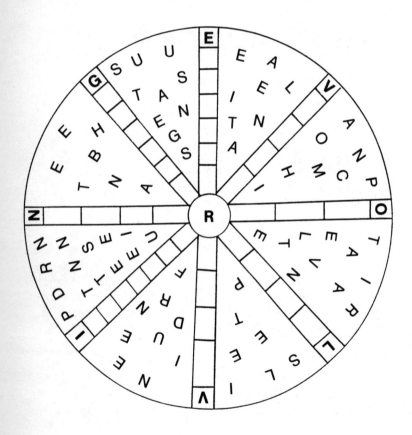

(ANSWER 58)

★★ 86 DOUBLE WORDS

Place a word in the brackets which, when placed on the end of the first word makes another word, and when placed at the front of the second word also makes another word.

FIRING (_ _ _) CUSHION
PLASTER (_ _ _ _) AWAY
PART (_ _ _ _) PIECE
POOR (_ _ _) COURT
CHURCH (_ _ _ _ _ _ _) JACK
SANDAL (_ _ _ _) LICE

(ANSWER 68)

★ 87 ELEVEN I

When the sums of the alternate digits of a number are equal, then that number is divisible by 11 exactly. For example 6325, where $6 + 2 = 3 + 5$.

Bearing this in mind, place the listed digits into the grid in such a way that each horizontal, vertical and corner-to-corner line is divisible by 11 exactly when read forwards or backwards. Remember that no multiplication or division is necessary. All you have to do is ensure that the sums of the alternate digits are equal.

1,   6,
2, 2, 2,   7,
3, 3, 3,   8, 8,
4, 4,   9.
5, 5,

(ANSWER 78)

★★★ **88 GROUPS II**

These group names have been mixed up.
Can you sort them?

WALK of GOATS
VOLERY of RAVENS
WATCH of BIRDS
TRIP of SNIPE
ASSEMBLANCE of NIGHTINGALES
UNKINDNESS of CLERGYMEN

(ANSWER 88)

★★ 89 SPIRAL

Although not a true Spiral, the figure below was, nevertheless, drawn by using nothing other than a piece of paper and a pair of compasses. Can you work out how this was done?

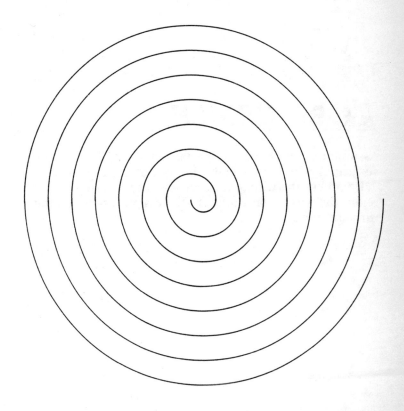

(*ANSWER* 98)

★★ 90 *GIRDLE*

Assume that the Earth is a perfect sphere with a smooth surface. A wire is stretched around it at the Equator.

If you cut the wire and insert a 2 yard length, then rejoin the wire, what would be the distance between the wire and the Earth?

(ANSWER 9)

★★★ 91 TILES II

Fit the nine Tiles together to make a Crossword.

(ANSWER 19)

★★ 92 CATEGORISE

Arrange these 15 words into five groups of three.

AMULET	CHARM	LATCH
ARREST	CLIP	PORTAL
BOLT	DOOR	SECURE
CAPTIVATE	ENTRANCE	TALISMAN
CATCH	GATE	TRINKET

(ANSWER 29)

★★★ 93 ALPHABET CROSSWORD II

Use all 26 letters of the alphabet to complete the Crossword. Five letters are already placed.

A B̸ C D E F G H I J̸ K L M
N O P Ø̸ R S T U V W X̸ Y Z̸

(ANSWER 39)

71

★★ 94 *ELEVEN II*

In Puzzle 87, the previous 'ELEVEN' Puzzle, we showed that when the sums of the alternate digits of a number are equal, the number is always divisible by 11.

However, it does not necessarily follow that every number which is divisible by 11 exactly has the sums of its alternate digits equal. As an example of this we present the number '987652413'. This number is exactly divisible by 11, even though the sums of its alternate digits are unequal.

There is, however, a further simple rule which will show that this number is divisible by 11 exactly, without the use of multiplication or division.

Can you determine what this simple rule is?

(*ANSWER* 49)

★★ 95 TARGET CROSSWORD II

Find sixteen 6-letter words by pairing up the thirty-two 3-letter bits.

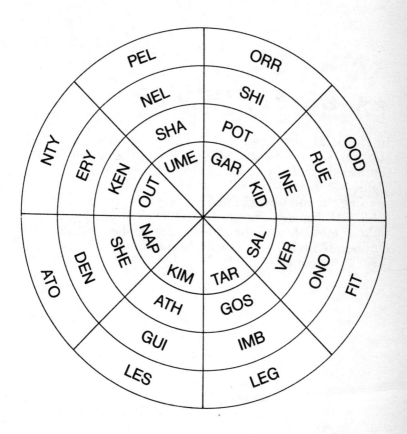

(ANSWER 59)

73

★★ 96 *ELEVEN III*

In Puzzle 94, the previous 'ELEVEN' Puzzle, we presented you with the number 987652413. This is the largest number divisible by 11 exactly to use 9 out of the 10 digits, 0-9, once each only.

Using the rules determined in the previous two 'ELEVEN' Puzzles (Puzzles 87 and 94), can you find, without multiplication or division, the smallest 9-digit number divisible by 11 exactly, to use 9 out of the 10 digits 0-9 once each only?

(ANSWER 69)

Commencing always with the centre letter 'A', spell out eight 11-letter words, travelling in any direction but always to an adjacent square, horizontally, vertically or diagonally. Each letter, apart from the centre letter 'A', may be used only once.

S	U	S	L	Y	G	L	A	U
S	U	O	I	S	N	Y	L	D
E	G	I	N	O	I	P	B	A
N	E	B	M	G	P	A	L	E
E	L	I	M	A	B	N	D	O
T	B	A	P	L	E	R	M	N
A	R	R	P	T	E	O	N	E
I	P	O	A	C	R	U	A	N
N	O	I	T	S	C	I	T	T

(ANSWER 79)

★ **98 SEQUENCE VI**

What are the next three letters in this sequence?

RIN, GEF, JIC, ROR, ? .

(ANSWER 89)

Spell out the 15-letter word by going into the Pyramid one room at a time. Go into each room once only. You may go into the passage as many times as you wish.

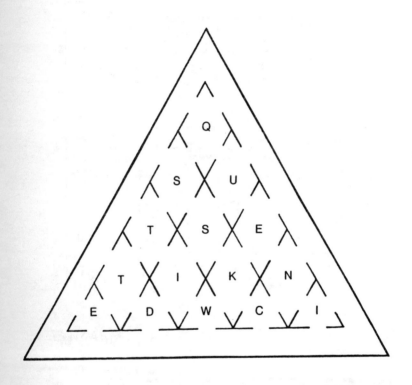

(ANSWER 99)

★ and ★★ **100 NUMBERS**

In each of the following, work out the missing number.

★ **(1)**

18	54	24
10	15	20
9	18	?

★★ **(2)**

6	4	9	6
16	4	8	8
8	4	2	4
27	3	9	?

(ANSWER 10)

The answers are all 9-letter words and will be found in the grid, one letter on each line, in order. Each letter is used only once.

E	B	P	F	P	P	L	G	L
E	M	R	R	U	R	O	R	L
I	B	R	A	O	F	O	R	I
T	Z	T	S	E	P	M	B	G
S	I	G	N	Z	O	L	W	E
T	E	T	A	R	T	S	L	A
U	N	U	O	C	A	T	F	I
F	N	D	T	I	T	I	S	A
E	N	E	H	E	E	E	L	S

1 Of wine, sparkling.
2 Heavy corded silk.
3 To make beautiful.
4 Eyeglasses with a handle.
5 Sulphur.
6 Empty remark.
7 A trunk.
8 German Air Force.
9 Never ceasing.

(ANSWER 20)

★★ 102 ONE HUNDRED PUZZLES

In each of the following, insert the numbers 1–9 inclusive, once each only, into the calculation to arrive at the answer 100.

A (‒) + + ‒ ‒ ‒   = 100

B   + + + ‒ ‒ ‒   = 100

C √ ‒ + ‒ ( ) (!) ‒ +   = 100

(ANSWER 30)

★★ 103 CLUELESS CROSSWORD

In each square are four letters. Your task is to cross out three of each four, leaving one letter in each square, so that the Crossword is made up in the usual way with good English interlocking words.

(ANSWER 40)

★ 104 THROW THE DIE

What are the chances of throwing a number greater than 4 with an ordinary die?

(ANSWER 50)

★★ 105 TRACK WORDS

Fill in the spaces to find the two 14-letter words. For each word, all letters are in the correct order and the overlapping letter appears twice. The word might appear reading clockwise or anticlockwise.

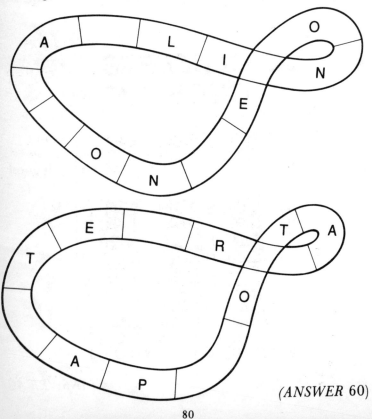

(ANSWER 60)

★★★ 106 THREE MEN

Three men in succession toss a coin. The winner is the first to throw a 'Head'.

    A goes first,
    B goes second,
    C goes third.

What are their respective chances of winning?

(ANSWER 70)

★★★ 107 BRAIN STRAIN

Insert numbers into the remaining blank squares in the grid so that all the calculations are correct, reading both across and down. All numbers to be inserted are less than 10.

	×		−		=	6
+	■	+	■	×	■	+
	÷		−	3	=	
−	■	−	■	÷	■	÷
	−	3	+		=	
=	■	=	■	=	■	=
6	−		−		=	

(ANSWER 80)

Replace the letters with numbers.

S N I P
N I P S
P I N S

It may be an addition sum or it may be a subtraction sum.

(ANSWER 90)

★★★ **109 THE EIGHTEEN TREES PUZZLE**

A gardener has a total of Eighteen Trees which he wishes to plant in straight rows of five trees in each row. The task which he sets himself is to plant the trees in such a way that he will obtain the maximum number of rows of five trees per row which are possible with an arrangement of eighteen trees. There are two slightly different ways in which he can achieve his task. Can you find both ways?

(ANSWER 100)

★★ 110 REVERSED

The 8-letter word of the title almost spells out another 8-letter word when reversed.
　　Can you think of an 8-letter word that does?

(ANSWER 106)

★★ 111 SQUARE II

Divide the Square into four identical sections. Each section must contain the same 9 letters, which can be arranged into a familiar 9-letter word.

S	N	V	E	N	L
E	U	R	U	L	A
I	E	I	A	V	U
L	S	A	I	R	I
V	U	R	S	S	E
A	R	N	V	L	N

(ANSWER 112)

★★ 112 ALPHAMETICS II

Replace the letters with numbers.

$$\begin{array}{r} \text{LABEL} \\ \text{ALL} \\ + \ \underline{\text{SEAL}} \\ \underline{\text{BALES}} \end{array}$$

(ANSWER 118)

★★ 113 CONNECTIONS II

Insert the numbers 0-12 in the circles, so that for any particular circle the sum of the numbers in the circles connected directly to it equals the value corresponding to the number in that circle, as given in the list.

Example: 1 = 14 (4+7+3)
4 = 8 (7+1)
7 = 5 (4+1)
3 = 1

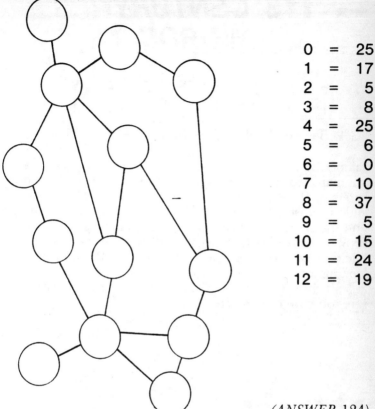

0	=	25
1	=	17
2	=	5
3	=	8
4	=	25
5	=	6
6	=	0
7	=	10
8	=	37
9	=	5
10	=	15
11	=	24
12	=	19

(ANSWER 124)

★ 114 *EARTH*

If the Earth were to be reduced in size to that of a golf ball or a billiard ball, with its mountains and deep sea rifts reduced in size proportionately, would it feel:

- **(a)** As smooth as a billiard ball?
- **(b)** Smoother than a billiard ball?
- **(c)** Not as smooth as a billiard ball?
- **(d)** Dimpled like a golf ball?
- **(e)** Rougher than a golf ball?

(ANSWER 130)

★★ 115 CENTURY WORDS

W	E	D	N	E	S	D	A	Y
|	|	|	|	|	|	|	|	|

23 + 5 + 4 + 14 + 5 + 19 + 4 + 1 + 25 = 100

Taking the value of letters A = 1, B = 2, C = 3, etc, there are many words in the English language, the sum of whose letters total 100. For example: LIGHTNING, QUARRY, and, as illustrated above, WEDNESDAY. However, can you find the shortest words in the English language (there are several) whose letters total 100? We will tell you that no 4-letter words are possible, so that the words you are looking for are 5-letters long. You should be familiar with at least three of these words, the remainder being either rare, obscure or obsolete.

(*ANSWER* 136)

★★★ 116 'U' FRAME

Each horizontal and vertical line contains the consonants of a word, not necessarily in order. The word can be completed by adding a number of 'U' vowels. The number at the end of each line indicates the number of consonants and 'U' vowels in the word you are looking for. For example, the number 41 means there are four consonants and one 'U' vowel.

Each letter in the grid may be used only once and all letters must be used.

Down

	1	2	3	4	5	6	7	8	
1	K	S	L	C	Z	P	Y	J	22
2	N	N	P	C	P	R	C	H	51
3	T	T	N	P	S	S	M	M	41
4	N	K	R	G	L	R	M	T	41
5	K	R	F	Y	T	M	S	Y	41
6	H	L	M	M	M	D	R	M	52
7	S	M	M	K	C	S	M	S	31
8	N	K	K	H	R	L	T	P	41
	41	41	41	41	41	51	41	41	

Across

Clues:

Across

1 African warrior.
2 Smash.
3 Trick.
4 Guttural sound.
5 Dirty brown.
6 Boring.
7 Scent.
8 Part of elephant.

Down

1 Animal.
2 Hide.
3 Untidy woman.
4 Fool.
5 Bunch of vegetation.
6 Crumples.
7 Ancient dead person.
8 Nervous.

(*ANSWER* 142)

★ 117 *HIDDEN ANAGRAM II*

If we presented you with the words 'MAR', 'AM', and 'FAR' and asked you to find the shortest English word which contained all the letters from which these words could be produced, we would expect you to come up with the word 'FARM'. Here is a further list of words:

ROSE, SYLPH, RUSTY, HURT

What is the shortest English word from which all these four words can be produced?

(ANSWER 148)

★★★ 118 HENRY FORD'S RUMINATION

(There is a clue to the keying of this Cryptogram in this title.)

JCHBD UDBIIJDB, NAB KGJNA IUBMSI
XABC NAB ODMLC LI HLIBCQMQBH, MCH,
IGKBXAMN JCXLNNLCQTE, NAB QBMDIALFN
LI LC DBWBDIB XABC LN IAGJTH OB LC
CBJNDMT.

(ANSWER 154)

★ 119 PYRAMID WORD III

Solve the five clues. Enter the correct words in the Pyramid and then rearrange all the letters to find a 15-letter word.

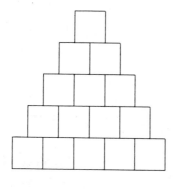

The indefinite article meaning one. (1)

Denoting similarity. (2)

Excavated. (3)
Bird of pigeon family. (4)

Spot or mark. (5)

(ANSWER 159)

★★★ 120 ALPHAMETICS III

Replace the letters with numbers.

```
   WEARY
   LAWYER
 + REALLY
   YAWNED
```

(ANSWER 102)

★ 121 NUMERALS

VII, V, VIII, VI, ? ,

What is next in the above sequence?

(ANSWER 108)

★★ 122 BULA'S TRUISMS

Rearrange the words to make a trite saying:

BEHOLDER IS IN THE ROOM, YET OF PIN-UPS, PLENTY OF THE BEAUTY FIND EYE.

(ANSWER 114)

★ 123 *LOGIC ANALOGY II*

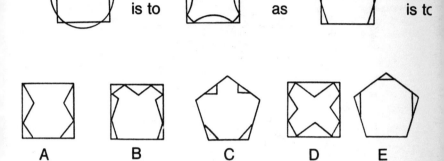

is to ___ as ___ is to

A   B   C   D   E

(ANSWER 120)

★★★ 124 *SEPTONIA*

In Septonia the alphabet runs from A to G, and the digits run from 1 to 7, plus 0 used as in our number system.

The district of Sevonia wishes to register its cars. The letters to be used are all of ABC in order, followed by four digits or less.

How many cars can be registered:

(a) Counting in the Septonia number system?
(b) Counting in our number system?

(ANSWER 126)

★★★ 125 MAGIC SQUARE II

Words spell the same across and down. Place the 25 letters in the Square to complete it. The Es have been placed for you.

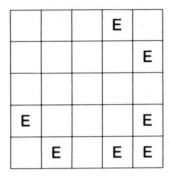

A A A A E̶

E̶ E̶ E̶ E̶ E̶

E̶ H L L M

M N N O O

R R T T Y

(ANSWER 132)

★ 126 *TRIOS*

Complete the words to find, in each set, three words which are synonyms. For example:

I N __ __ N __   **Answer:** INVENT
__ __ I __ I N __ __ __   ORIGINATE
__ __ __ I __ N   DESIGN

1   P __ E __ __ P __ __ __ __ __
    P E __ P E __ __ __ __ __ __ __ __
    __ __ E E P

2   C __ __ __ __ T __
    C __ __ T __ __ __
    C __ __ T __ __ T

3   F I __ __ I __ I __ __ __
    __ __ __ I F I __ I __ __
    F __ __ __ I __ __ __ __ __

4   T E __ __ E __ __ T E
    __ __ __ E __ __ T E
    __ E __ T __ __ __ __ __ E __

5   I __ T __ I __ __ T __
    __ __ __ __ __ __ I __ __ T __ __
    __ I __ __ I __ __ __ T

(ANSWER 138)

93

Place the letters in the grid to complete the Crossword.

	E		A		E	
E	■	U	■	T	■	O
	O		N		D	
O	■	G	■	T	■	D
	N		Q		A	
R	■	O	■	T	■	E
	U		S		T	

A	B	D	D
E	E	L	N
O	R	S	S
S	T	U	U

(ANSWER 144)

★★ 128 ANAGRAM THEME II

Arrange the 14 words in pairs so that each pair is an Anagram of another word or name. The seven words produced will have a linking theme. For example, if the words 'TRY' and CREASE' appeared in the list they could be paired to form the word 'SECRETARY' and the theme could be PROFESSIONS.

CAP	GREAT	NINE	RAIN
CRY	HER	NO	RIOT
DRAIN	IS	PEEP	
GEAR	MAN	PLAIN	

(ANSWER 150)

★★ 129 ALPHABET X-WORD II

Place the letters of the alphabet in the X-Word to complete the words, using each letter once only.

A B C D E F G H I J K L M
N O P Q R S T U V W X Y Z

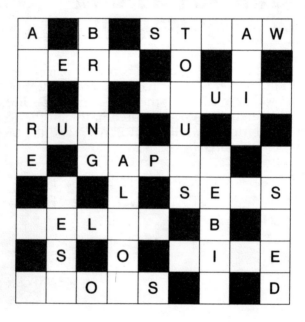

(ANSWER 155)

★ 130 SHADES

Complete the following, which are all Colour Shades, then arrange the initial letters to find a seventh colour shade.

     _ Y _ T _ R
     _ Q _ A _ A _ I _ E
     _ U _ S _ T
     _ U _ M _ G
     _ C _ R _
     _ O _ H _

(ANSWER 103)

★ 131 NETWORK II

Start anywhere and travel along the connecting lines in a continuous path to adjacent circles to spell out a 14-letter word. Every circle must be visited once only.

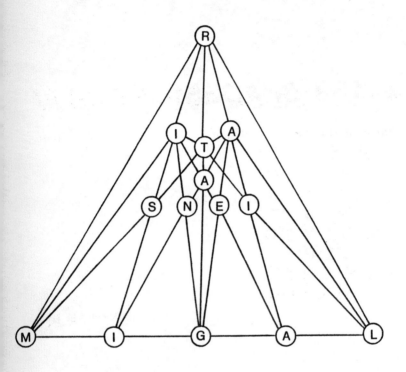

(*ANSWER* 109)

★★★ 132 ALPHAMETICS IV

Replace the letters with numbers.

```
      C O P S
     C L O S E
   C E L L A R
   C O R P S E
       C A S E
 + C O L L A R
   R E C T O R
```

(*ANSWER* 115)

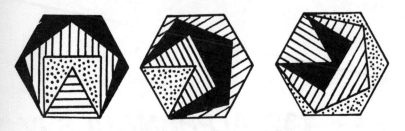

Which figure below continues the above sequence?

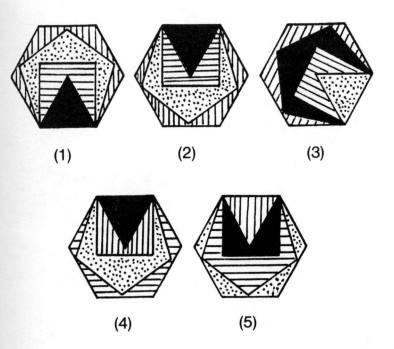

(1)   (2)   (3)

(4)   (5)

(ANSWER 121)

★★★ 134 *GEORGE BERNARD SHAW'S REASONING*

(There is a clue to the keying of this Cryptogram in the title.)

UJB DBGICFGEQB RGF GHGSUI JLRIBQN UC
UJB KCDQH: UJB VFDBGICFGEQB CFB
SBDILIUI LF UDYLFA UC GHGSU UJB KCDQH
UC JLRIBQN.

(*ANSWER* 127)

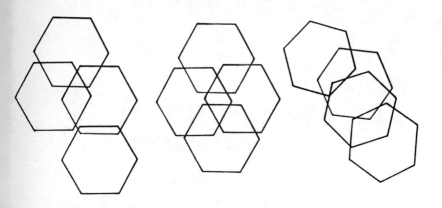

Which figure below continues a Sequence which is
occurring in the figures above?

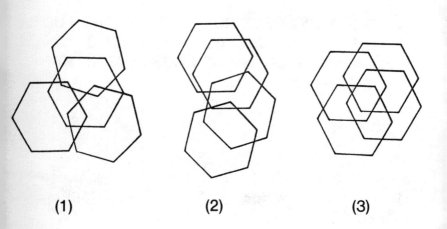

(1)   (2)   (3)

(ANSWER 133)

★★★ 136 *UNIVERSAL ANAGRAM*

A Universal Anagram is one that makes a new word commencing with each of its letters in turn. **Example:**

STOP
TOPS
OPTS
POST

Can you find a 5-letter Universal Anagram?

(ANSWER 139)

★ 137 *REBUS II*

Find the word.

(ANSWER 145)

★★ 138 PHOBIAS

There are well over 700 known Phobias, some much better known than others. For example, most people would know that CLAUSTROPHOBIA is an abnormal fear of confined spaces, but very few would know that ARACHYBUTYRO-PHOBIA is the fear of eating a Peanut Butter Sandwich lest the gooey Peanut Butter sticks to the roof of one's mouth.

In Column 'A' is a list of Fears and in Column 'B' a list of Phobias. Can you match them up correctly?

A	B
Speed	SIDERODROMOPHOBIA
Lightning	PHASMOPHOBIA
Thunder	THALASSOPHOBIA
Horses	TACOPHOBIA
Ghosts	GALEOPHOBIA
Crowds	ASTRAPOPHOBIA
Sea	DORAPHOBIA
Trains	KERAUNOPHOBIA
Sharks	OCHLOPHOBIA
Fur	HIPPOPHOBIA

(*ANSWER* 151)

★ 139 X-WORD II

In the X-Word below, all of the black squares have been replaced with letters. You have to find the black squares.

S	T	R	O	B	E	D	S	I	S	T	E	R
E	S	E	X	E	R	C	I	S	E	R	V	E
L	I	N	E	A	R	S	L	I	N	E	A	L
F	E	D	C	R	E	E	L	S	U	M	P	I
S	E	E	R	I	D	A	Y	A	L	O	N	G
L	I	R	A	P	A	T	Y	P	E	R	T	I
A	N	T	V	I	A	L	S	E	A	T	S	O
U	I	T	E	N	S	P	L	A	S	H	I	U
G	L	A	D	I	M	O	O	D	E	A	R	S
H	E	R	E	I	A	M	B	S	A	P	I	N
T	Y	R	A	N	T	R	E	L	A	P	S	E
E	Y	E	X	T	E	N	S	I	L	E	A	S
R	O	D	E	O	S	T	E	M	E	N	D	S

(*ANSWER* 156)

★★★ **140 PLUS AND MINUS**

There are 12 ways in which all the nine digits 1-9 inclusive, can be used once each only in the correct order, using the Plus and Minus symbols only, to produce the answer 100. One of these ways is:

$$12 + 3 + 4 + 5 - 6 - 7 + 89 = 100$$

How many of the other 11 ways can you find?

(ANSWER 104)

Complete the word in each column; all the words end in 'R'.

The scrambled letters in the section to the right of each column are an anagram of a word which will give you a clue to the word you are trying to find, in the column.

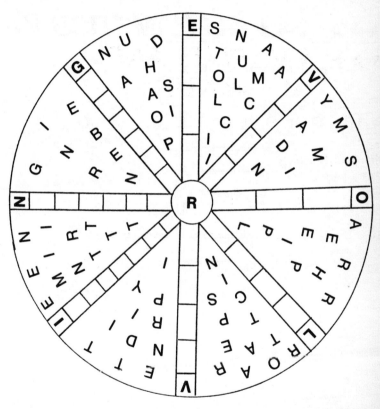

(*ANSWER* 110)

★★★ 142 *ALPHAMETICS V*

Replace the letters with numbers.

```
F R O G)  G U L P E D   (F L Y
          _ _ _ _
          _ _ _ _ _
          _ _ _ _ G
          _ _ _ U _
          _ _ _ P _
              _ P _
```

(*ANSWER* 116)

★★ 143 SHUNTING PUZZLE

Start at position (1) and, by Shunting, find the shortest possible number of moves to finish at Position (2).

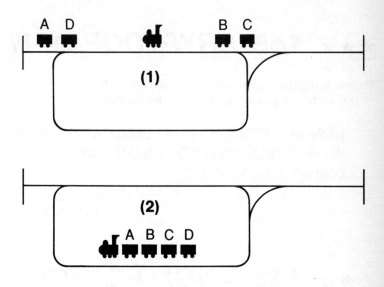

(ANSWER 122)

★★★ 144 ACES

What are the chances that, if 2 cards are drawn in succession from a pack of 52 playing cards (without returning the first card) then both are Aces?

(*ANSWER* 128)

★★★ 145 CRYPTOGRAM III

This is a straight substitution cryptogram where each letter of the alphabet has been replaced by another.

NQNUR XUYSMLWGYI YO ENIGMA TMAW DN
WZN XUYSMLWGYI YO NIWZMAGVAT.
DNIHVTGI SGAUVNBG

(*ANSWER* 134)

★★★ 146 ANGLO-SAXON RIDDLE

My twin points are joined together by crooked iron. With the wind I wrestle, with the depth of the sea I fight. I search out the midmost water, and I bite the very ground itself. What am I?

(*ANSWER* 140)

★★ 147 3-LETTER WORDS

What have these 3-letter words in common?

SAW, DEW, RED, LOP.

(ANSWER 146)

★★ 148 SOMETHING IN COMMON II

What do these words have in common?

MAP, DINE, YAK, ASSET, GEM.

(ANSWER 152)

★★ 149 FABRICS

The following are all types of Fabric. When you have solved them, rearrange the first letters of each to find another type of Fabric.

```
_ A _ I _ O
_ C _ Y _ I _
_ N _ O _ A
_ I _ L _
_ O _ L _ N
_ S _ R _ K _ A _
```

(ANSWER 157)

★★★ 150 MISSING LETTERS II

Fill in the Missing Letters. All words have Mineral connections.

1 _ O _ N _ L _ N _ E
2 _ T _ L _ C _ I _ E
3 _ O _ R _ A _ I _ E
4 _ H _ S _ H _ R _ S
5 _ I _ E _ T _ N _
6 _ E _ E _ R _ T _
7 _ O _ A _ S _ U _
8 _ I _ C _ B _ E _ D _
9 _ E _ P _ N _ I _ E
10 _ A _ G _ N _ S _

(*ANSWER* 105)

★★★ 151 SHAPES

A one-word description of 'in the shape of an eagle's beak' is 'AQUILINE'. Can you complete the following one-word descriptions?

In the shape of:	Description:
A spiral	_ O _ U _ E
A sword	_ I _ H _ I _
A pear	_ Y _ I _ O _ M
A helmet	_ A _ E _ T _
A boat	_ A _ I _ U _ A _
A diamond	_ H _ M _ O _ D _ L
Fingers	_ I _ I _ A _ E
A knife blade	_ U _ T _ A _ E
A tongue	_ I _ G _ L _ T _
A snail's shell	_ O _ H _ E _ T _
A horn	_ O _ N _ A _
A bow	_ R _ U _ T _
The teeth of a saw	_ E _ R _ T _
A hand	_ A _ M _ T _
A berry	_ A _ C _ F _ R _

(*ANSWER* 111)

★★★ 152 HIDDEN WORDS

Hidden in the statement, below, are the names of 7 Trees. Can you find them?

"Stop burglar, chase them, lock the car, obstruct two live bony welders, man goes wild."

(*ANSWER* 117)

★ **153** *PAIRS*

Each word in List A can be linked up with a word in List B, for the same reason. Work out the reason and then pair up the 23 sets of words.

List A	List B
TOUCH	ONLY
FUN	FLOW
MILK	MISS
FAIR	DAY
DOWN	SEEK
STAND	GO
ONE	PRISMS
PUSH	OUT
WELL	HONEY
FAST	BUTTER
OPEN	OUT
UP	GAMES
EBB	PARCEL
HIDE	CRY
LAW	DELIVER
HIT	UNDER
OVER	DRAKES
PART	FURIOUS
NIGHT	SQUARE
BREAD	ORDER
PRUNES	TRULY
DUCKS	SHUT
HUE	SHOVE

(*ANSWER* 123)

114

★★★ 154 PAIR WORDS

Each word in List A has two possible Pair Words with List B and each word in List B has two possible Pair Words in List A.

Can you find the two sets of 10 pairs?

List A	List B
STAGE	GROUND
GLOVE	COACH
SHOE	HAND
HORSES	FOOT
PAD	JOCKEY
PLAY	LEATHER
SADDLE	FOX
WRIST	LOCK
EARTH	ACTOR

(*ANSWER* 129)

In the small circle in the example, the words 'ONCOST', STRIPE' and 'PERSON' are arranged clockwise, each overlapping by two letters. From the eight clues given below, which are in no particular order, find eight 6-letter words which, when placed in the correct order round the large circle, in a clockwise direction, will overlap by two letters as shown in the example.

Example

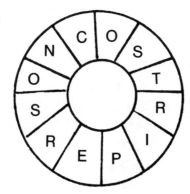

The belief in one God as creator and ruler.

Go back.

Plant with prickly leaves and head.

Scarcity.

Pass by.

Kiss and cuddle.

Safe.

Pure and decent.

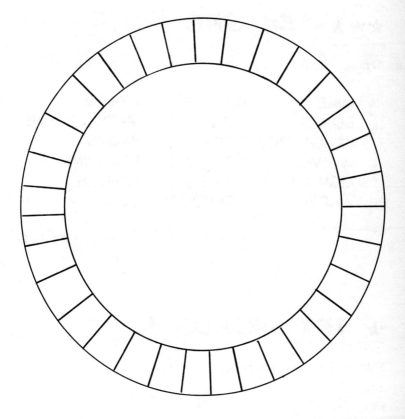

(*ANSWER* 135)

★★★ 156 GROUPS III

Arrange the following into collective(!) groups of three.

MICE	GROUSE	HYENAS
BOARS	LIONS	MACHINE GUNS
KANGAROOS	ROOKS	WASPS
WOLVES	WILD PIGS	PENGUINS
MONKEYS	SWINE	WHALES
WHITING	PORPOISES	SEALS

(ANSWER 141)

★ 157 WORDS II

Which word completes the following list?

FACET, AZURE, CUBAN, ERASE, ? ,

(ANSWER 147)

★★★ 158 *HEXAGON II*

Fit the listed words into the six spaces encircling the appropriate number on the diagram so that each word correctly interlinks with the two words on either side (you will see that each word has two consecutive letters in common with the word on its side). (**Note:** to arrive at the correct solution some words will have to be entered clockwise and some anticlockwise.)

NATION
NURSES
RIOTER
SENSOR
RUNNER
MITRES
NUANCE
TIMERS
DEMIST
MISTER
TENNER
SORTED

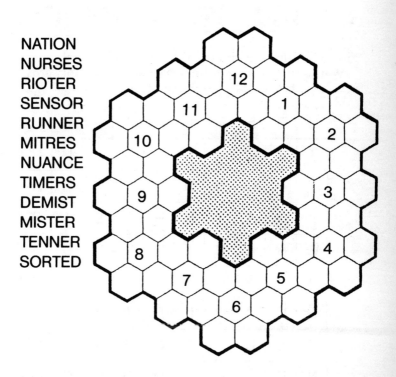

(*ANSWER* 153)

★ 159 PREFIX

Find one word which, when placed in front of each of the following words, will make another word.

TIGHT, WHEEL, WORKS, WINGS, MARK.

(*ANSWER* 158)

★★ 160 WORD SEARCH

Find 17 Cities, which are, or have been, Capitals.
   Words run in straight lines backwards and forwards, vertically, horizontally, and diagonally.

O	B	E	T	A	K	A	S	U	L
T	E	O	N	S	I	S	V	U	U
T	L	D	N	O	N	A	X	U	H
A	G	A	I	N	R	E	B	I	S
W	R	K	U	V	M	E	H	U	I
A	A	A	O	B	E	Z	B	T	D
D	D	R	O	L	E	T	X	A	A
E	E	U	V	W	S	R	N	Y	G
N	R	A	N	G	O	O	N	O	O
G	U	A	T	E	M	A	L	A	M

(*ANSWER* 160)

PUZZLE NUMBERS AND ANSWER NUMBERS

Each puzzle has a Puzzle Number and an Answer Number. Each Answer has an Answer Number and a Puzzle Number.

Puzzle Number	Answer Number	Puzzle Number	Answer Number	Puzzle Number	Answer Number	Puzzle Number	Answer Number
1	101	41	14	81	18	121	108
2	107	42	24	82	28	122	114
3	113	43	34	83	38	123	120
4	119	44	44	84	48	124	126
5	125	45	54	85	58	125	132
6	131	46	64	86	68	126	138
7	137	47	74	87	78	127	144
8	143	48	84	88	88	128	150
9	149	49	94	89	98	129	155
10	1	50	5	90	9	130	103
11	11	51	15	91	19	131	109
12	21	52	25	92	29	132	115
13	31	53	35	93	39	133	121
14	41	54	45	94	49	134	127
15	51	55	55	95	59	135	133
16	61	56	65	96	69	136	139
17	71	57	75	97	79	137	145
18	81	58	85	98	89	138	151
19	91	59	95	99	99	139	156
20	2	60	6	100	10	140	104
21	12	61	16	101	20	141	110
22	22	62	26	102	30	142	116
23	32	63	36	103	40	143	122
24	42	64	46	104	50	144	128
25	52	65	56	105	60	145	134
26	62	66	66	106	70	146	140
27	72	67	76	107	80	147	146
28	82	68	86	108	90	148	152
29	92	69	96	109	100	149	157
30	3	70	7	110	106	150	105
31	13	71	17	111	112	151	111
32	23	72	27	112	118	152	117
33	33	73	37	113	124	153	123
34	43	74	47	114	130	154	129
35	53	75	57	115	136	155	135
36	63	76	67	116	142	156	141
37	73	77	77	117	148	157	147
38	83	78	87	118	154	158	153
39	93	79	97	119	159	159	158
40	4	80	8	120	102	160	160

ANSWERS

1 *WORD CONNECTIONS*

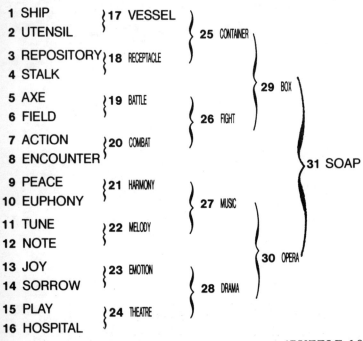

1 SHIP
2 UTENSIL
3 REPOSITORY
4 STALK
5 AXE
6 FIELD
7 ACTION
8 ENCOUNTER
9 PEACE
10 EUPHONY
11 TUNE
12 NOTE
13 JOY
14 SORROW
15 PLAY
16 HOSPITAL

17 VESSEL
18 RECEPTACLE
19 BATTLE
20 COMBAT
21 HARMONY
22 MELODY
23 EMOTION
24 THEATRE

25 CONTAINER
26 FIGHT
27 MUSIC
28 DRAMA

29 BOX
30 OPERA

31 SOAP

(PUZZLE 10)

2 *PYRAMID QUOTATION*

F, BE, HOP, VAMP, THEME, THESIS,
SWEETEN, RESIDENT, BATTALION.

(PUZZLE 20)

3 MIDDLE WORDS

1 KIN, 2 ON, 3 NECK, 4 RING, 5 RATE,
6 LOCK, 7 HER, 8 ROT, 9 ANT,
10 HORN.

(PUZZLE 30)

4 CRYPTOGRAM I

THERE IS NO MAN LIVING WHO ISN'T
CAPABLE OF DOING MORE THAN HE THINKS
HE CAN DO.

HENRY FORD

Key:

A	B	C	D	E	F	G	H	I	J	K	L	M
D	M	Y	F	L	T	Q	J	X	G	N	A	V

N	O	P	Q	R	S	T	U	V	W	X	Y	Z
R	C	I	U	Z	E	S	K	W	P	O	H	B

(PUZZLE 40)

5 *THREE DICE*

5 in 108.

6 – 6 – 3	5 – 6 – 4
6 – 3 – 6	5 – 5 – 5
6 – 4 – 5	4 – 6 – 5
6 – 5 – 4	4 – 5 – 6
5 – 4 – 6	3 – 6 – 6

10 in 216   (6 × 6 × 6).

(PUZZLE 50)

6 *A TOUR OF THE USA*

Oregon, Connecticut, Oklahoma, Montana, Wyoming, Massachusetts, Delaware, Tennessee, Ohio, Mississippi, Texas, Virginia, Louisiana, Hawaii, Arkansas, Indiana, Georgia, Alabama, Pennsylvania, Vermont, Iowa, Idaho.

(PUZZLE 60)

7 THE LARGEST CIRCLE

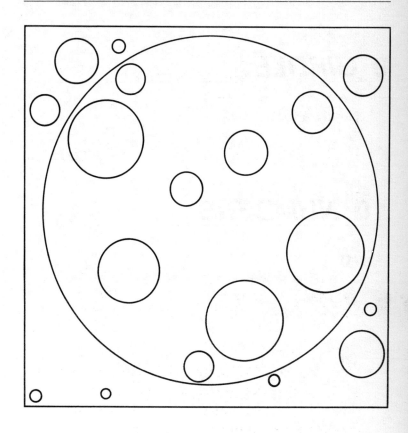

(*PUZZLE* 70)

8 ODD ONE OUT

FALL.   The rest are herbs with the addition of
        an initial letter,
        i.e. (C)LOVE, (D)ILL, (S)AGE, (M)ACE.

(*PUZZLE* 80)

9 GIRDLE

Nearly a foot.

(PUZZLE 90)

10 NUMBERS

(1) 6

$18 \div 9 \times 5 = 10$

$54 \div 18 \times 5 = 15$

$24 \div \boxed{6} \times 5 = 20$

(2) 9

$\sqrt[3]{6 \times 4 \times 9} = 6$

$\sqrt[3]{16 \times 4 \times 8} = 8$

$\sqrt[3]{8 \times 4 \times 2} = 4$

$\sqrt[3]{27 \times 3 \times 9} = \boxed{9}$

(PUZZLE 100)

11 *TILES I*

S	P	A	T		S	O	A	K
M	A	P		G		K	I	N
O	P	E	R	A		A	T	E
G			Z		P		W
	N	E	M	E	S	I	S	
F		N		L				F
L	A	D		L	E	V	E	L
E	W	E		E		E	R	A
W	E	D	S		S	T	E	W

(*PUZZLE* 11)

12 FLANNEGAN'S FINAGLING FACT

```
F L A N N E G A N ' S   F I  N A G L I  N G   F A C T
A B C D   E F     G     H                         I  J
```

Key:

A	B	C	D	E	F	G	H	I	J	K	L	M
C	K	I	L	E	A	F	M	H	N	O	B	P

N	O	P	Q	R	S	T	U	V	W	X	Y	Z
D	Q	R	S	T	G	J	U	V	W	X	Y	Z

THAT QUANTITY WHICH, WHEN
MULTIPLIED BY, DIVIDED BY, ADDED TO, OR
SUBTRACTED FROM THE ANSWER YOU GET,
GIVES YOU THE ANSWER YOU SHOULD
HAVE GOTTEN.

(PUZZLE 21)

13 TARGET CROSSWORD I

OMELET, OUTWIT, RUCKUS, RUBBER,
SHAGGY, VERMIN, BATTEN, BEYOND,
CATKIN, CUPOLA, ICICLE, HOOVES,
IMPACT, INFANT, GRAVEL, FLETCH.

(PUZZLE 31)

14 WORD POWER I

1	HONEYCOMB	6	PROMINENT
2	TAXIMETER	7	TRIMESTER
3	PHRENETIC	8	MEDITATED
4	NOVENNIAL	9	PELMANISM
5	SEQUESTER		

(PUZZLE 41)

15 BLOCK TOTAL

FI VES
6 7 8 2 3

(PUZZLE 51)

16 MISSING LETTERS I

1	BOLIVIANO	6	KOPECK
2	CENTAVO	7	NAPOLEON
3	GUILDER	8	SCHILLING
4	SESTERTIUM	9	SESTERTII
5	SOVEREIGN	10	ROUBLE

(PUZZLE 61)

17 SEQUENCE IV

364.

Start at the smallest even square number and add subsequent even square numbers:

4, (+16) 20, (+36) 56, (+64) 120, (+100) 220, (+144) 364,

(PUZZLE 71)

18 *HEXAGON I*

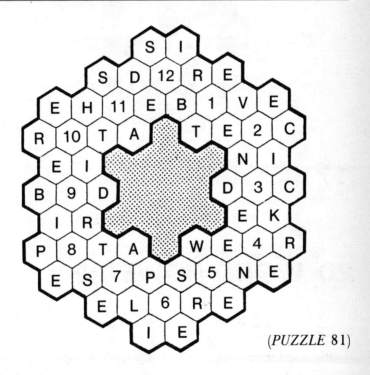

(*PUZZLE* 81)

19 TILES II

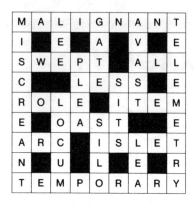

(*PUZZLE* 91)

20 WORD POWER II

1	FRIZZANTE	6	PLATITUDE
2	GROSGRAIN	7	PROBOSCIS
3	EMBELLISH	8	LUFTWAFFE
4	LORGNETTE	9	PERPETUAL
5	BRIMSTONE		

(*PUZZLE* 101)

21 SEQUENCE I

147.

Each number commences with the next consecutive even number. Each number then becomes a sequence by dividing by 2. The number produced is then divided by 2 and this continues until an odd number is produced. e.g. 8 ÷ 2 = 4, 84 ÷ 2 = 42, 8442 ÷ 2 = 4221. As 4221 is an odd number, the sequence stops at 84424221.

(PUZZLE 12)

22 WORDS I

They are all names of animals with the middle letter missing.

A(S)S, HO(R)SE, TI(G)ER, SA(B)LE.

(PUZZLE 22)

23 HIDDEN ANAGRAM I

BACKGROUND.

(PUZZLE 32)

24 SOMETHING'S THE SAME

In each word the second, third and seventh letters spell out the name of an animal:

B<u>RA</u>CKE<u>T</u> (RAT), C<u>AP</u>ABL<u>E</u> (APE), S<u>PI</u>CIN<u>G</u> (PIG), C<u>RA</u>NIU<u>M</u> (RAM), R<u>EW</u>RIT<u>E</u> (EWE).

(PUZZLE 42)

25 SEQUENCE II

15625.

A list of numbers which are both cubes and squares.

i.e. 1^2, 8^2, 27^2, 64^2, 125^2,

or 1^3, 4^3, 9^3, 16^3, 25^3,

(PUZZLE 52)

26 *SYNCHRONISED SYNONYMS*

FRIENDLY, OBLIGING
CONTINUE, LENGTHEN
CONTRIVE, INTRIGUE
MYTHICAL, ROMANTIC
DEFINITE, EXPLICIT
CARELESS, SLAPDASH
EXCITING, RIVETING
DOCILITY, MILDNESS

(PUZZLE 62)

27 DIY X-WORD

S	L	A	P		S	P	E	W
L	A	P		P		R	O	E
I	M	P	R	U	D	E	N	T
P		E		T		S		S
	T	A	P		A	C	E	
A		L		M		R		B
C	R	I	N	O	L	I	N	E
H	E	N		W		B	I	T
E	D	G	Y		P	E	T	S

(*PUZZLE* 72)

28 WHAT'S IN A NAME?

Colours:	OLIVE, SANDY, ISABEL.
Birds:	MARTIN, ROBIN, MAVIS.
Flowers:	PRIMROSE, POPPY, MYRTLE.
Gems:	GARNET, DIAMOND, PEARL.

(PUZZLE 82)

29 CATEGORISE

Arrange into groups of synonyms:

1 ENTRANCE, CHARM, CAPTIVATE.
2 GATE, DOOR, PORTAL.
3 AMULET, TALISMAN, TRINKET.
4 SECURE, ARREST, CATCH.
5 BOLT, LATCH, CLIP.

(PUZZLE 92)

30 ONE HUNDRED PUZZLES

A $(7-5)^2 + 96 + 8 - 4 - 3 - 1 = 100$

B $3^2 + 91 + 7 + 8 - 6 - 5 - 4 = 100$

C $\sqrt{9} - 6 + 72 - (1)(3!) - 8 + 45 = 100$

(PUZZLE 102)

31 LOGIC

11	4	16	5
6	10	1	9
2	13	8	15
12	7	14	3

(PUZZLE 13)

32 ALPHABET CROSSWORD I

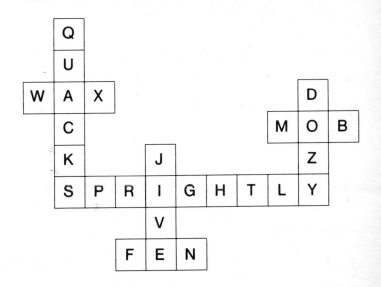

(PUZZLE 23)

141

33 *MEASLE FISH*

184 926. (It makes no difference how many of
the fish are Male or how many are Female
because 37 is one third of 111 !)

(PUZZLE 33)

34 *MAGIC NUMBER SQUARE*

17	24	1	8	15
23	5	7	14	16
4	6	13	20	22
10	12	19	21	3
11	18	25	2	9

(PUZZLE 43)

35 'E' FRAME

Across
1 DECREE
2 SECEDE
3 EMERGE
4 EYELET
5 BEETLE
6 CHEESE

Down
1 NEEDLE
2 FEELER
3 WHEEZE
4 LESSEE
5 WEEPER
6 VENEER

(PUZZLE 53)

36 SENTENCE

The vowels A, E, I, O, U are used in succession.

(PUZZLE 63)

37 *NOVEL WORD POWER*

TIPPET	PURSY
HUBRIS	RUCHE
ENCOMIUM	OPTATIVE
FLACCID	TRACT
OCCIDENT	ORIEL
UNCTUOUS	CHILIAD
RETICULE	OAKUM
TIPSTAFF	LEGHORN
HAUBERK	

THE FOURTH PROTOCOL (by Frederick Forsyth).

(PUZZLE 73)

38 *PYRAMID WORD II*

15-letter word: PROGNOSTICATION.

(PUZZLE 83)

39 ALPHABET CROSSWORD II

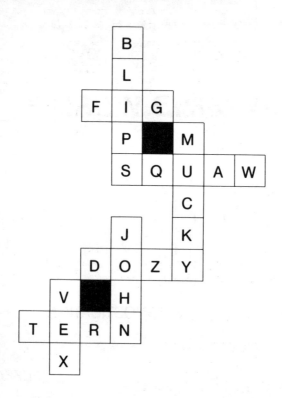

(*PUZZLE* 93)

40 *CLUELESS CROSSWORD*

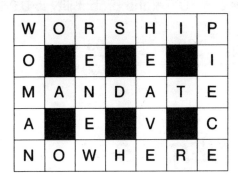

(*PUZZLE* 103)

41 *COMMON CLUES*

They all have 'DOUBLE' in the answer.

1 DOUBLE ENTRY
2 DOUBLE DUTCH
3 DOUBLE-DEALING
4 DOUBLE-CHECK
5 DOUBLE-TALK
6 DOUBLE-DECKER
7 DOUBLE-BASS
8 DOUBLE AGENT
9 DOUBLE-QUICK
10 DOUBLE-CROSS

(*PUZZLE* 14)

42 TARGET

49 times in 50 (i.e. the probability is 0.98).

$$\frac{8}{100} + \frac{90}{100} = \frac{98}{100}$$

(PUZZLE 24)

43 MINERALS

BAUXITE, ALABASTER, CORUNDUM, ISINGLASS, PYRITE, MALACHITE.

(PUZZLE 34)

44 ANAGRAM THEME I

The theme is NATIONALITIES:

DANISH	(HAD, SIN)
BELGIAN or BENGALI	(GALE, NIB)
CHILEAN	(INCH, ALE)
ENGLISH	(SHIN, LEG)
MALTESE	(SEAL, MET)
SPANISH	(SASH, PIN)
ALGERIAN	(ANGER, AIL)

(PUZZLE 44)

45 *SOMETHING IN COMMON I*

They are the 'ends' of Countries:

GER(MANY), BAH(RAIN), TUR(KEY),
KU(WAIT), NOR(WAY).

(PUZZLE 54)

46 *LOGIC ANALOGY I*

C.

The figure at the back changes places with the
figure at the front i.e.

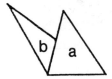 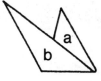

(PUZZLE 64)

47 *ENIGMAGRAM*

LEMONADE, MUSCATEL, VERMOUTH, ABSINTHE.

The fifth anagram is DRAMBUIE.

(*PUZZLE 74*)

48 *ALLSORTS*

Muses: CALLIOPE, TERPSICHORE, URANIA, EUTERPE.

Virtues: PRUDENCE, TEMPERANCE, FORTITUDE, CHARITY.

Zodiac: LIBRA, CAPRICORN, SCORPIO, CANCER.

Heraldry: FYLFOT, CHEVRON, ERMINE, HERALD.

(*PUZZLE 84*)

49 ELEVEN II

Taking alternate digits:

$9 + 7 + 5 + 4 + 3 = 28$
$8 + 6 + 2 + 1 \quad\quad = 17$

As the difference between the sums of these two sets of digits is 11, the number is divisible by 11 exactly.

This would also apply if the difference between the sums of the two sets of digits was any multiple of 11.

(PUZZLE 94)

50 THROW THE DIE

1 in 3.

$1 - 2 - 3 - 4 -$ ⑤ $-$ ⑥ (2 in 6).

(PUZZLE 104)

51 ZOETROPE

For example:

TOG – JEW
BOON – REED
MELON – CUBED

(*PUZZLE* 15)

52 CRAZY COLUMNS

The missing numbers reading downwards are 13, 8, 45 and 33.

There are four separate sequences in the table, but these alternate between columns.

Sequence One:	The **Fibonacci Sequence** alternates between columns one and three i.e. 0, 1, 1, 2, 3, 5, 8, 13, 21, 34, 55, 89.
Sequence Two:	**Prime Numbers** alternate between columns two and four i.e. 2, 5, 7, 11, 13, 17, 19, 23, 29, 31, 37, 41.
Sequence Three:	**Pyramid Numbers** alternate between columns three and one i.e. 1, 3, 6, 10, 15, 21, 28, 36, 45, 55, 66, 78.
Sequence Four:	The **Three Times Table** alternates between columns four and two i.e. 3, 6, 9, 12, 15, 18, 21, 24, 27, 30, 33, 36.

Notes:

1 The Fibonacci Sequence is formed by adding together the two previous numbers to continue the sequence, i.e. 0, 1, (0+1) 1, (1+1) 2, (1+2) 3, (2+3) 5, (3+5) 8, etc.

2 Prime Numbers are numbers starting with 2 that are divisible only by themselves and 1.

3 Pyramid or Triangular numbers are numbers which can be arranged in a triangle (See diagram).
i.e. 1, 3, 6, 10, 15, 21, 28, 36, 45, 55, 66, 78.

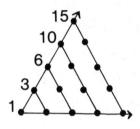

(PUZZLE 25)

53 *COMPLETE THE CALCULATION*

$6^4 \div 48 = 27$

$(6^4 = 1296)$

(PUZZLE 35)

54 REBUS I

CAMELOPARD   (a giraffe).

C A M E Ø ʂ L O P ɇ ¢ A R D

(*PUZZLE* 45)

55 DOG

The dog cost £15.

Say the Kennel cost £x
and the Dog cost £y

Then $x = \dfrac{x + 5 + y}{3}$

and $y = \dfrac{3(x + y - 5)}{4}$

Then $2x - y = 5$
and $3x - y = 15$

$x = 10$
$y = 15$

(*PUZZLE* 55)

56 DOG RACE

720.   (6 × 5 × 4 × 3 × 2 × 1)

(*PUZZLE* 65)

57 NETWORK I

TRANSCENDENTAL.

(*PUZZLE* 75)

58 REVOLVING I

EMBITTER   (ALIENATE)
VICTOR   (CHAMPION)
OTHER   (ALTERNATIVE)
LETTER   (EPISTLE)
VULGAR   (UNREFINED)
INSPECTOR   (SUPERINTENDENT)
NETHER   (BENEATH)
GRANDEUR   (AUGUSTNESS)

(*PUZZLE* 85)

59 *TARGET CROSSWORD II*

GARDEN, GOSPEL, GUITAR, IMBRUE,
ORRERY, OUTFIT, OODLES, KENNEL,
KIDNAP, LEGUME, KIMONO, SALINE,
SHANTY, SHEATH, SHIVER, POTATO.

(*PUZZLE* 95)

60 *TRACK WORDS*

RECONCILIATION, PASTEURISATION.

(*PUZZLE* 105)

61 *COLOUR MATCH*

TUESDAYS are shaded YELLOW. The days are shaded to match the colours of the spectrum (rainbow):

SUNDAY	RED
MONDAY	ORANGE
TUESDAY	YELLOW
WEDNESDAY	GREEN
THURSDAY	BLUE
FRIDAY	INDIGO
SATURDAY	VIOLET

(PUZZLE 16)

62 *RIDDLE*

A Heroine.

(PUZZLE 26)

63 *PYRAMID I*

PARLIAMENTARIAN

(PUZZLE 36)

64 *THREE NAMES*

The alternate letters spell out words:

OSWALD = OWL SAD
CLAIRE = CAR LIE
PIERRE = PER IRE

(PUZZLE 46)

65 *CRYPTOGRAM II*

A GOOD MEMORY IS NOT AS GOOD AS A
LITTLE INK.

CHINESE PROVERB

Key:

A	B	C	D	E	F	G	H	I	J	K	L	M
N	X	F	O	G	C	W	M	S	A	L	H	R

N	O	P	Q	R	S	T	U	V	W	X	Y	Z
B	K	V	I	D	U	Z	Q	E	Y	J	T	P

(PUZZLE 56)

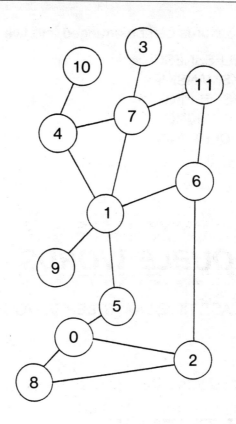

(*PUZZLE* 66)

67 GROUP PUZZLE

The 15 words can be arranged into five words:

CARELESSNESS
MARKSMANSHIP
OVERSTEPPING
FREETHINKING
BLOODLETTING

(*PUZZLE 76*)

68 DOUBLE WORDS

PIN, CAST, TIME, LAW, STEEPLE, WOOD.

(*PUZZLE 86*)

69 ELEVEN III

102347586.   1 + 2 + 4 + 5 + 6 = 18
             0 + 3 + 7 + 8   = 18

(*PUZZLE 96*)

70 THREE MEN

A   4 in 7.
B   2 in 7.
C   1 in 7.

(To answer this question you'll need to know
about Infinite Series because, in theory, A, B and
C could go on tossing 'for ever' and always
throwing 'Tails'.)

(PUZZLE 106)

71 RIDDLE

A Puff-adder

(PUZZLE 17)

72 WORD CIRCLE

MEDIOCRE, ORDINARY.

(PUZZLE 27)

73 ANAGRAMMED SYNONYMS

1   SHIFT – DISPLACE
2   MEAN – MISERABLE
3   TALE – ANECDOTE
4   LUCK – FORTUNE
5   DUEL – ENCOUNTER
6   RASP – ABRADE
7   YET – MOREOVER
8   FORT – CITADEL
9   DOER – ACHIEVER
10 PEAL – RESONATE

(PUZZLE 37)

74 SQUARE I

T	E	E	S	I	R
V	R	E	V	I	S
E	E	I	T	E	V
S	E	E	E	E	T
T	T	I	T	V	E
R	R	S	E	T	T

SERVIETTE

(PUZZLE 47)

75 MONEY

Jack had £1.80 and Jill had £1.40.

Let x pence = Jack's money.
and y pence = Jill's money.

$$x = 75 + \tfrac{3}{4}y$$
$$y = 50 + \tfrac{1}{2}x$$
$$\therefore y = 50 + \frac{75 + \tfrac{3}{4}y}{2}$$
$$\therefore 2y = 100 + 75 + \tfrac{3}{4}y$$
$$1\tfrac{1}{4}y = 175$$
$$y = 140$$
$$\therefore x = 75 + \tfrac{3}{4}y$$
$$x = 75 + 105$$
$$x = 180$$

(*PUZZLE 57*)

76 BOOKS

There were 2 Red Books and 11 Blue Books.

Let Red = x Books
    Blue = y Books

Then, $49x + 39y = 527$

The only solution is $x = 2, y = 11$.

(*PUZZLE* 67)

77 SEQUENCE V

The number of surfaces increases by one each time. The figure shown here has five surfaces: four sides and a base.

(*PUZZLE* 77)

78 ELEVEN I

5	3	4	6
2	8	9	3
1	7	8	2
4	2	3	5

Variations are possible.

(*PUZZLE 87*)

79 JUMBLE II

APPLAUDABLE, ABANDONMENT,
AERONAUTICS, ALTERCATION,
APPROPRIATE, AMIABLENESS,
AMBIGUOUSLY, AGONISINGLY.

(*PUZZLE 97*)

80 BRAIN STRAIN

5	×	2	−	4	=	6
+		+		×		+
8	÷	2	−	3	=	1
−		−		÷		÷
7	−	3	+	3	=	7
=		=		=		=
6	−	1	−	4	=	1

(PUZZLE 107*)*

81 NO REPEAT LETTERS

PHLEGMATIC

(PUZZLE 18*)*

82 *LETTERS*

1 in 6   (SENT, TENS, NETS, NEST, in the 24
possible arrangements)
(5 in 24 if you've included the 'proper noun'
STEN)

(*PUZZLE* 28)

83 *CEREAL*

60p.

Say it cost the supermarket x pence. Then the
profit was ($x^2/100$) pence.

So, $x^2/100 = 96 - x$
$\therefore \quad x = 60$

(*PUZZLE* 38)

84 *FAMILY*

Clarence was Terence's grandson.

(*PUZZLE* 48)

85 PYRAMID WORD I

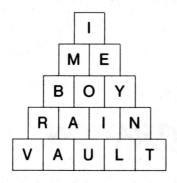

15-letter word: MANOEUVRABILITY.

(PUZZLE 58)

86 MAGIC SQUARE I

T	R	A	M	P
R	O	T	O	R
A	T	O	N	E
M	O	N	K	S
P	R	E	S	S

(PUZZLE 68)

87 CONCENTRATION

E

(PUZZLE 78)

88 GROUPS II

TRIP of GOATS
UNKINDNESS of RAVENS
VOLERY of BIRDS
WALK of SNIPE
WATCH of NIGHTINGALES
ASSEMBLANCE of CLERGYMEN

(PUZZLE 88)

89 SEQUENCE VI

GEB.

They are the first two letters of the first name and the first letter of the second name of the last five Presidents of the United States of America:
RICHARD NIXON, GERALD FORD,
JIMMY CARTER, RONALD REAGAN,
GEORGE BUSH.

(PUZZLE 98)

90 ALPHAMETICS I

$$
\begin{array}{r}
9108 \\
- \quad 1089 \\
\hline
8019 \\
\hline
\end{array}
$$

(PUZZLE 108)

91 COLOURS

3 in 34. $(^{10}\!/_{17} \times {}^{9}\!/_{16} \times {}^{8}\!/_{15} \times {}^{7}\!/_{14} = {}^{3}\!/_{34})$

(PUZZLE 19)

92 *MAGIC WITHIN MAGIC WITHIN MAGIC*

1	63	62	4	5	59	58	8
56	15	49	48	19	44	20	9
55	47	25	39	38	28	18	10
11	22	36	30	31	33	43	54
53	42	32	34	35	29	23	12
13	24	37	27	26	40	41	52
14	45	16	17	46	21	50	51
57	2	3	61	60	6	7	64

(PUZZLE 29)

93 SEQUENCE II

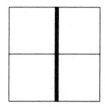

They are the even numbers 2, 4, 6, 8, complete with mirror image.

e.g.

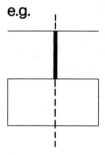

(*PUZZLE* 39)

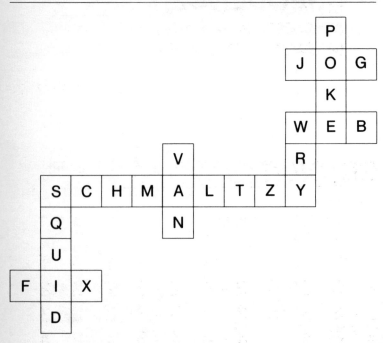

(PUZZLE 49)

95 CARGO BOAT

(a)   0.0004   ($\frac{2}{100} \times \frac{2}{100}$)

(b)   0.0392 $2(\frac{2}{100} \times \frac{98}{100})$

(c)   0.9604   ($\frac{98}{100} \times \frac{98}{100}$)

(*PUZZLE* 59)

96 DICE

6 in 36   (or 1 in 6).

1 - 6	1 - 5	1 - 4	1 - 3	1 - 2	1 - 1
2 - 6	2 - 5	2 - 4	2 - 3	2 - 2	2 - 1
3 - 6	3 - 5	3 - 4	3 - 3	3 - 2	3 - 1
(4 - 6)	4 - 5	4 - 4	4 - 3	4 - 2	4 - 1
(5 - 6)	(5 - 5)	5 - 4	5 - 3	5 - 2	5 - 1
(6 - 6)	(6 - 5)	(6 - 4)	6 - 3	6 - 2	6 - 1

(*PUZZLE* 69)

(*PUZZLE* 79)

98 SPIRAL

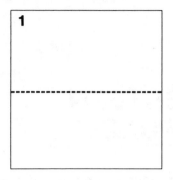

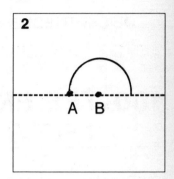

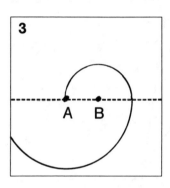

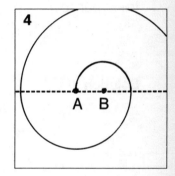

1   Fold the paper in half.

2   With the compass point on B, draw a semi-circle.

3   With the compass point on A, draw another semi-circle which joins up with the first semi-circle.

4   Continue in this way, alternating between Points A and B, until the spiral is formed.

(PUZZLE 89)

99 *PYRAMID II*

QUICKWITTEDNESS.

(PUZZLE 99)

100 *THE EIGHTEEN TREES PUZZLE*

Both these solutions produce nine rows of five trees per row.

Solution 1

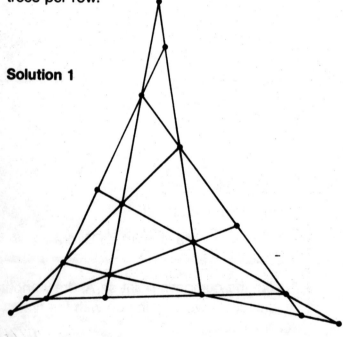

Solution 2

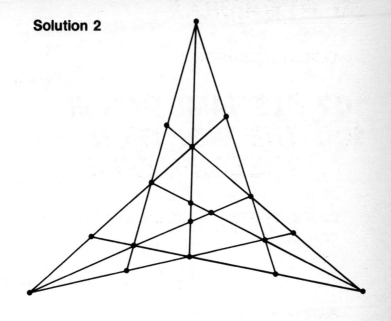

(PUZZLE 109)

101 *JUMBLE I*

DETERIORATE, DOCUMENTARY,
DOMINEERING, DOORKNOCKER,
DOWNTRODDEN, DRESSCIRCLE,
DEVOTEDNESS, DEIFICATION.

(PUZZLE 1)

102 *ALPHAMETICS III*

```
      8  1  7  2  9
   6  7  8  9  1  2
+  2  1  7  6  6  9
   ─────────────────
   9  7  8  3  1  0
```

(PUZZLE 120)

103 *SHADES*

OYSTER, AQUAMARINE, RUSSET, NUTMEG, OCHRE, MOCHA.

Anagram: MAROON.

(PUZZLE 130)

104 *PLUS AND MINUS*

$123 - 45 - 67 + 89$	=	100
$123 + 4 - 5 + 67 - 89$	=	100
$123 + 45 - 67 + 8 - 9$	=	100
$1 + 23 - 4 + 56 + 7 + 8 + 9$	=	100
$12 - 3 - 4 + 5 - 6 + 7 + 89$	=	100
$1 + 23 - 4 + 5 + 6 + 78 - 9$	=	100
$1 + 2 + 34 - 5 + 67 - 8 + 9$	=	100
$123 - 4 - 5 - 6 - 7 + 8 - 9$	=	100
$12 + 3 - 4 + 5 + 67 + 8 + 9$	=	100
$-1 + 2 - 3 + 4 + 5 + 6 + 78 + 9$	=	100
$1 + 2 + 3 - 4 + 5 + 6 + 78 + 9$	=	100

(PUZZLE 140)

105 *MISSING LETTERS II*

1   HORNBLENDE
2   STALACTITE
3   TOURMALINE
4   PHOSPHORUS
5   LIMESTONE
6   METEORITE
7   POTASSIUM
8   PITCHBLENDE
9   SERPENTINE
10 MANGANESE

(PUZZLE 150)

106 *REVERSED*

DESSERTS and STRESSED.

(*PUZZLE* 110)

107 *GREAT WORDS*

NOBLE, GLORIOUS, AUGUST, TREMENDOUS, COLOSSAL, IMMENSE, ILLUSTRIOUS, GRAND.

Anagram: GIGANTIC.

(*PUZZLE* 2)

108 *NUMERALS*

II.   They are the numerals attached to the last five British Monarchs: Edward VII, George V, Edward VIII, George VI and Elizabeth II.

(*PUZZLE* 121)

109 *NETWORK II*

EGALITARIANISM.

(*PUZZLE* 131)

110 *REVOLVING II*

ERROR	(MISCALCULATION)
VIGOUR	(DYNAMISM)
OUTER	(PERIPHERAL)
LINGER	(PROCRASTINATE)
VALOUR	(INTREPIDITY)
IRREGULAR	(INTERMITTENT)
NEWCOMER	(BEGINNER)
GOSSAMER	(DIAPHANOUS)

(PUZZLE 141)

111 *SHAPES*

Spiral – VOLUTE
Sword – XIPHOID
Pear – PYRIFORM
Helmet – GALEATE
Boat – NAVICULAR
Diamond – RHOMBOIDAL
Fingers – DIGITATE
Knife blade – CULTRATE
Tongue – LINGULATE
Snail's shell – COCHLEATE
Horn – CORNUAL
Bow – ARCUATE
Teeth of a saw – SERRATE
Hand – PALMATE
Berry – BACCIFORM

(PUZZLE 151)

112 SQUARE II

S	N	V	E	N	L
E	U	R	U	L	A
I	E	I	A	V	U
L	S	A	I	R	I
V	U	R	S	S	E
A	R	N	V	L	N

UNIVERSAL

(PUZZLE 111)

113 ALPHABET X-WORD I

(PUZZLE 3)

114 BULA'S TRUISMS

BEAUTY IS IN THE EYE OF THE BEHOLDER,
YET PIN-UPS FIND PLENTY OF ROOM.

(PUZZLE 122)

115 ALPHAMETICS IV

```
            2  7  3  0
         2  9  7  0  4
      2  4  9  9  1  8
      2  7  8  3  0  4
            2  1  0  4
+  2  7  9  9  1  8
   _____
   8  4  2  6  7  8
```

(*PUZZLE* 132)

116 ALPHAMETICS V

```
2  1  0  5  )  5  8  7  4  3  6  (  2  7  9
               4  2  1  0
            _____
               1  6  6  4  3
               1  4  7  3  5
            _____
                  1  9  0  8  6
                  1  8  9  4  5
               _____
                        1  4  1
               _____
```

(*PUZZLE* 142)

117 *HIDDEN WORDS*

Larch, Hemlock, Carob, Olive, Ebony, Elder, Mango.

(PUZZLE 152)

118 *ALPHAMETICS II*

```
    3  7  4  1  3
          7  3  3
+     9  1  7  3
   ─────────────
    4  7  3  1  9
```

(PUZZLE 112)

119 *LETTER CHANGE*

1 BREAK THE BANK
2 LEND AN EAR
3 TAKE TO HEART
4 MY FOOT
5 WITH A BANG
6 NOT A HOPE
7 IN HOT WATER
8 KEEP YOUR HAIR ON
9 FLOG A DEAD HORSE
10 GO TO POT
11 MAKE TRACKS FOR
12 PULL A FAST ONE
13 A PIG IN A POKE
14 FALL IN WITH
15 CAP IN HAND
16 LIVE IT UP
17 PLAY SAFE
18 PEACE OF MIND
19 IN FULL SWING
20 TURN UP TRUMPS

(PUZZLE 4)

120 *LOGIC ANALOGY II*

B. Anything outside the square in the first figure
is folded into the square in the second figure.

(PUZZLE 123)

(4).

Explanation:
The figure turns from base to base, i.e.

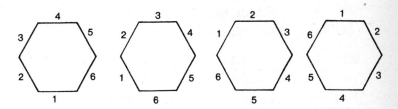

and the different shadings move in the following sequence:

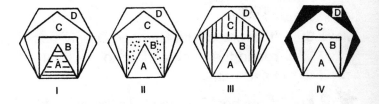

I: Horizontal Stripes – areas A, B, C, D in turn.
II: Dots – areas B, A, D, C in turn.
III: Vertical Stripes – areas C, D, A, B in turn.
IV: Black – areas D, C, B, A in turn.

Note: Stripes are horizontal or vertical viewed from Side 1.

(*PUZZLE* 133)

122 *SHUNTING PUZZLE*

The quickest method is in seven moves.

Move 1: The Engine moves to couple up with Carriages A and D.

Move 2: It reverses with Carriages A and D and shunts Carriages B and C up to the right-hand buffer.

Move 3: It pushes Carriages A and D round a complete circuit of the track and couples them up with Carriages B and C.

Move 4: It reverses with Carriages D, A, B and C down to the bottom part of the circuit.

Move 5: It reverses with Carriage D only back round the track and up to the right-hand buffer.

Move 6: It pushes Carriage D to the end of Carriages A, B and C at the bottom of the track.

Move 7: It reverses on its own, round a complete circuit and, facing in the required direction, couples up with Carriages A, B, C and D.

(*PUZZLE* 143)

123 *PAIRS*

TOUCH and GO, FUN and GAMES,
MILK and HONEY, FAIR and SQUARE,
DOWN and OUT, STAND and DELIVER,
ONE and ONLY, PUSH and SHOVE,
WELL and TRULY, FAST and FURIOUS,
OPEN and SHUT, UP and UNDER,
EBB and FLOW, HIDE and SEEK,
LAW and ORDER, HIT and MISS,
OVER and OUT, PART and PARCEL,
NIGHT and DAY, BREAD and BUTTER,
PRUNES and PRISMS, DUCKS and DRAKES,
HUE and CRY.

(PUZZLE 153)

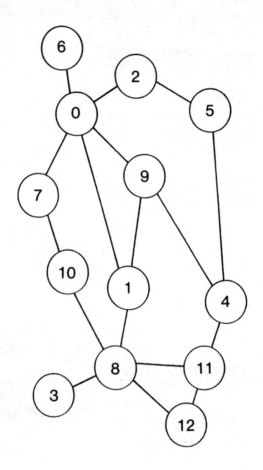

(*PUZZLE* 113)

125 *THREE TOO MANY*

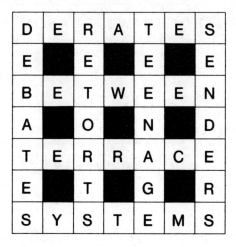

D	E	R	A	T	E	S
E	■	E	■	E	■	E
B	E	T	W	E	E	N
A	■	O	■	N	■	D
T	E	R	R	A	C	E
E	■	T	■	G	■	R
S	Y	S	T	E	M	S

(PUZZLE 5)

126 *SEPTONIA*

(a) 7777   (octal)
(b) 4095   (decimal)

(PUZZLE 124)

127 *GEORGE BERNARD SHAW'S REASONING*

GEORGE BERNARD SHAW'S REASONING
ABCD   E   FG H IJ K   L

Key:

A	B	C	D	E	F	G	H	I	J	K	L	M
G	E	M	H	B	N	A	J	L	O	P	Q	R

N	O	P	Q	R	S	T	U	V	W	X	Y	Z
F	C	S	T	D	I	U	V	W	K	X	Y	Z

THE REASONABLE MAN ADAPTS HIMSELF TO
THE WORLD: THE UNREASONABLE ONE
PERSISTS IN TRYING TO ADAPT THE WORLD
TO HIMSELF.

(PUZZLE 134)

128 *ACES*

	1	in	221

	4	in	52
×	3	in	× 51
	12	in	2652

(PUZZLE 144)

194

129 *PAIR WORDS*

Answer No. 1				Answer No. 2
PLAY	—	GROUND	—	EARTH
HORSES	—	COACH	—	STAGE
GLOVE	—	HAND	—	WRIST
PAD	—	FOOT	—	SHOE
SADDLE	—	JOCKEY	—	HORSES
SHOE	—	LEATHER	—	SADDLE
EARTH	—	FOX	—	GLOVE
WRIST	—	LOCK	—	PAD
STAGE	—	ACTOR	—	PLAY

(*PUZZLE* 154)

130 *EARTH*

(b) Smoother than a billiard ball.

(*PUZZLE* 114)

131 *QUICK CALCULATION*

In the sequence 1 to 100, ie 1, 2, 3, 4, . . ., 97, 98, 99, 100, opposite pairs of numbers total 101. As there are fifty such pairs, the sum of all the numbers is 50 × 101 = 5050.

(PUZZLE 6)

132 *MAGIC SQUARE II*

H	A	R	E	M
A	T	O	N	E
R	O	Y	A	L
E	N	A	T	E
M	E	L	E	E

(PUZZLE 125)

(1) Which contains four triangles. The number of triangles in the figures increases by one each time.

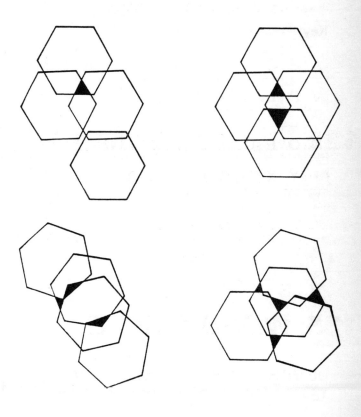

(*PUZZLE* 135)

134 *CRYPTOGRAM III*

EVERY PRODUCTION OF GENIUS MUST BE
THE PRODUCTION OF ENTHUSIASM.
BENJAMIN DISRAELI

Key:

A	B	C	D	E	F	G	H	I	J	K	L	M
V	D	L	S	N	O	E	Z	G	H	P	B	T

N	O	P	Q	R	S	T	U	V	W	X	Y	Z
I	Y	X	F	U	A	W	M	Q	J	C	R	K

(PUZZLE 145)

135 *WORD CIRCLE*

DEARTH, THEISM, SMOOCH, CHASTE,
TEASEL, ELAPSE, SECURE, RECEDE.

(PUZZLE 155)

136 *CENTURY WORDS*

Familiar: BUZZY, NUTTY, PUSSY.

Rare: STUTT, (Obsolete verb – Oxford
                             English Dictionary)
            TOTTY, TOUSY,
            TUTTS, (Plural of obsolete noun –
                             Oxford English Dictionary)
            YOUST.

(PUZZLE 115)

137 *GROUPS I*

GAGGLE	of	GEESE
HUSK	of	HARES
KNOT	of	TOADS
MURDER	of	CROWS
LABOUR	of	MOLES
MUSTER	of	PEACOCKS

(PUZZLE 7)

138 *TRIOS*

1. PRECIPITOUS
   PERPENDICULAR
   STEEP

2. COMPETE
   CONTEND
   CONTEST

3. FICTITIOUS
   ARTIFICAL
   FABRICATED

4. TEMPERATE
   MODERATE
   RESTRAINED

5. INTRICATE
   COMPLICATED
   DIFFICULT

(PUZZLE 126)

139 *UNIVERSAL ANAGRAM*

T I M E S

I T E M S

M I T E S

E M I T S

S M I T E

(PUZZLE 136)

140 ANGLO-SAXON RIDDLE

An anchor.

(*PUZZLE* 146)

141 GROUPS III

PACK	of	GROUSE WOLVES HYENAS
POD	of	WHALES WHITING PORPOISES
NEST	of	MICE WASPS MACHINE GUNS
ROOKERY	of	PENGUINS ROOKS SEALS
SOUNDER	of	BOARS SWINE WILD PIGS
TROOP	of	KANGAROOS LIONS MONKEYS

(*PUZZLE* 156)

142 'U' FRAME

Down

	1	2	3	4	5	6	7	8	
1	K	S	L	C	Z	P	Y	J	ZULU
2	N	N	P	C	P	R	C	H	CRUNCH
3	T	T	N	P	S	S	M	M	STUNT
4	N	K	R	G	L	R	M	T	GRUNT
5	K	R	F	Y	T	M	S	Y	RUSTY
6	H	L	M	M	M	D	R	M	HUMDRUM
7	S	M	M	K	C	S	M	S	MUSK
8	N	K	K	H	R	L	T	P	TRUNK

Across

S	S	F	C	C	S	M	J
K	K	R	H	L	L	U	U
U	U	U	U	U	U	M	M
N	L	M	M	M	M	M	P
K	K	P	P	P	P	Y	Y
					S		

(*PUZZLE* 116)

202

143 *FIND THE LOGIC*

14	①	7	4
③	12	9	16
10	15	5	13
6	8	11	②

So that:

1 No two consecutive numbers appear in any horizontal, vertical or diagonal line.

From which it follows that:

2 No two consecutive numbers appear in adjacent (horizontal, vertical, diagonal) squares.

(*PUZZLE* 8)

144 *SEVENS*

(*PUZZLE* 127)

145 *REBUS II*

STANCHION

F̷I̷S̷T̷B̷R̷A̷N̷C̷H̷O̷N̷ION

(*PUZZLE* 137)

146 *3-LETTER WORDS*

They can all be typed using adjacent (including diagonally adjacent) keys on a standard 'QWERTY' typewriter keyboard.

(*PUZZLE* 147)

147 *WORDS II*

TENET: The words will then form a Magic Word Square when placed one under the other:

F A C E T
A Z U R E
C U B A N
E R A S E
T E N E T

(*PUZZLE* 157)

148 *HIDDEN ANAGRAM II*

UPHOLSTERY.

(*PUZZLE* 117)

149 *PRONOUNS*

USHERS: US, SHE, HE, HER, HERS.

(PUZZLE 9)

150 *ANAGRAM THEME II*

The theme is FRUIT:

APRICOT	(CAP, RIOT)
MANDARIN	(DRAIN, MAN)
CHERRY	(CRY, HER)
ORANGE	(NO, GEAR)
TANGERINE	(GREAT, NINE)
RAISIN	(IS, RAIN)
PINEAPPLE	(PLAIN, PEEP)

(PUZZLE 128)

151 *PHOBIAS*

Speed – TACOPHOBIA
Lightning – ASTRAPOPHOBIA
Thunder – KERAUNOPHOBIA
Horses – HIPPOPHOBIA
Ghosts – PHASMOPHOBIA
Crowds – OCHLOPHOBIA
Sea – THALASSOPHOBIA
Trains – SIDERODROMOPHOBIA
Sharks – GALEOPHOBIA
Fur – DORAPHOBIA

(*PUZZLE* 138)

152 *SOMETHING IN COMMON II*

They are all Girls' Names, reversed.

(*PUZZLE* 148)

153 *HEXAGON III*

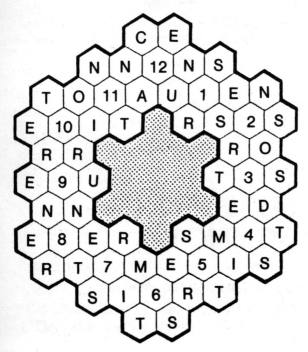

(*PUZZLE* 158)

154 *HENRY FORD'S RUMINATION*

```
H E N R Y    F O R D ' S    R U M I N A T I O N
A B C D E    F G   H I      J K L   M N
```

Key:

A	B	C	D	E	F	G	H	I	J	K	L	M
M	O	P	H	B	F	Q	A	L	R	S	T	K

N	O	P	Q	R	S	T	U	V	W	X	Y	Z
C	G	U	V	D	I	N	J	W	X	Y	E	Z

UNDER PRESSURE, THE MOUTH SPEAKS
WHEN THE BRAIN IS DISENGAGED, AND,
SOMEWHAT UNWITTINGLY, THE GEARSHIFT
IS IN REVERSE WHEN IT SHOULD BE IN
NEUTRAL.

(PUZZLE 118)

155 ALPHABET X-WORD II

(*PUZZLE* 129)

★ 156 *X-WORD II*

S	T	R	O	B	E		S	I	S	T	E	R
E		E	X	E	R	C	I	S	E	R		E
L	I	N	E	A	R		L	I	N	E	A	L
F		D		R	E	E	L	S		M		I
S	E	E	R		D	A	Y		L	O	N	G
L		R	A	P		T		P	E	R		I
A			V	I	A		S	E	A			O
U		T	E	N		P		A	S	H		U
G	L	A	D		M	O	O		E	A	R	S
H		R		I	A	M	B	S		P		N
T	Y	R	A	N	T		E	L	A	P	S	E
E		E	X	T	E	N	S	I	L	E		S
R	O	D	E	O	S		E	M	E	N	D	S

(PUZZLE 139)

157 FABRICS

CALICO
ACRYLIC
ANGORA
LISLE
POPLIN
ASTRAKHAN

Anagram: ALPACA

158 PREFIX

WATER.

159 *PYRAMID WORD III*

15-letter word: DISADVANTAGEOUS.

(*PUZZLE* 119)

160 *WORD SEARCH*

LUXEMBOURG	GABERONE
MONTEVIDEO	ATHENS
BELGRADE	DUBAI
RANGOON	BONN
LUSAKA	ADEN
GUATEMALA	OSLO
MOGADISHU	BERN
OTTAWA	SUVA
DAKAR	

(*PUZZLE* 160)

YOUR SCRATCHPAD